Technical guidance on the safe use of lifting equipment offshore

HSE Books

Contents

Introduction

Who should read this guidance

1   This guidance provides technical information for those involved in the supply, operation and control of lifting equipment in the offshore environment, and shows how to apply the Lifting Operations and Lifting Equipment Regulations 1998 (LOLER)[1] and the Provision and Use of Work Equipment Regulations 1998 (PUWER)[2] offshore. The guidance is primarily aimed at dutyholders, offshore installation managers (OIMs), managers, supervisors, competent persons and operatives involved with the operation and safe use of lifting equipment offshore. Others who may find this guidance useful are:

■   people working for contractors;
■   equipment suppliers;
■   safety representatives;
■   verification bodies; and
■   equipment manufacturers.

What this guidance covers

2   This guidance applies to all offshore installations, both fixed and mobile, operating within the United Kingdom Continental Shelf. Some typical examples are:

■   fixed platforms, either manned or of normally unattended status;
■   mobile installations, eg semi-submersibles, jack-ups, accommodation units and floating production, storage and offloading vessels;
■   pipe-laying vessels;
■   crane barges and crane lifting vessels;
■   well service vessels;
■   other installations subject to the Health and Safety at Work etc Act 1974 (Application Outside Great Britain) Order 2001 (AOGBO).[3]

3   It does not apply to seagoing ships and supply boats, for which the Maritime and Coastguard Agency (MCA)[4] has jurisdiction. Lifting equipment on these vessels which is part of the ship's equipment used by the crew (such as that used for loading, unloading, fuelling or provisioning) is not covered by LOLER. Some specific examples of vessels not included in this guidance are:

■   standby vessels;
■   shuttle tankers;
■   dredgers; and
■   tugs, anchor handling and survey vessels.

4   It is not possible in this guidance to cover every type of ship or seagoing vessel. You should contact the Health and Safety Executive (HSE) or the Maritime and Coastguard Agency for advice on whether PUWER and LOLER apply to your particular activities.

5   Appropriate sections of this guidance shall be applicable to lifting equipment that is used in conjunction with diving operations and other subsea activities that could be carried out from diving and ROV support vessels. Diving operations and sub-sea activities come under LOLER by virtue of the Health and Safety at Work etc Act 1974 (Application Outside Great Britain) Order 2001. It should be noted that the HSG221 guidance does not cover lifting equipment specifically installed on vessels for the deployment of divers. The term 'lifting equipment' as covered in this guidance includes lifting accessories, portable lifting equipment, personnel transfer carriers and lifting equipment used for offshore drilling operations. It does not include:

■   fork-lift trucks;
■   offshore containers and their associated sling sets;
■   winch units used for the launch/recovery of survival craft such as TEMPSC and other emergency evacuation systems.

6   'Lifting operations' in this guidance does not include manual handling. This is covered by the Manual Handling Operations Regulations 1992[5] and associated guidance.[6]

How you should use this guidance

7   The use of lifting equipment, both onshore and offshore, is covered by the Lifting Operations and Lifting Equipment Regulations 1998 (LOLER) and the Provision and Use of Work Equipment Regulations 1998 (PUWER) together with their respective Approved Codes of Practice[7,8] (ACOPs). These ACOPs set out how you can comply with the Regulations in a general sense, and you will need to refer to them. This guidance will help you find out in detail how to apply these Regulations specifically to offshore lifting equipment and its associated operations.

8   This guidance summarises the most important parts of LOLER (see Appendix 1) and has been arranged around specific topics which will give you practical advice about the management, selection and safe operation of lifting equipment and accessories. Appendix 1 contains a checklist which links the guidance to the main requirements of LOLER and PUWER, and the glossary in Appendix 2 explains the industry terminology that has been used. This guidance does not introduce higher standards or impose any additional requirements to the existing regulations. It aims to clarify what the law requires and illustrates methods for achieving compliance.

Major regulations and 'dutyholder'

9   The two most important sets of regulations applying to offshore lifting equipment are LOLER and PUWER. They apply onshore to all premises and work situations where the Health and Safety at Work etc Act 1974 (the HSW Act) applies. Offshore they apply to installations, wells, pipelines etc operating within the territorial waters of Great Britain and in designated areas of the UK Continental Shelf in accordance with AOGBO. LOLER specifically deals with lifting equipment and lifting operations. PUWER also applies to the provision and use of lifting equipment and covers other important aspects, such as providing information, instructions, training and maintenance.

10   LOLER and PUWER both place duties on employers, which may bring contractors, consultants, suppliers, verification bodies etc within scope of the Regulations as they all employ people to work offshore. Offshore-specific legislation, such as the Offshore Installations and Pipeline Works (Management and Administration) Regulations 1995 (MAR),[9] adopts a different approach, and places duties on the 'dutyholder'. This term is uniquely applied offshore, and is defined as the operator of a fixed installation and the owner of a mobile installation. If the dutyholder is an employer, who employs people to work on the installation, they will have responsibilities under LOLER and PUWER for their own employees.

11   The dutyholder is required to appoint a manager - the Offshore Installation Manager (OIM) - to command and control the installation and to be responsible for health and safety on a day-to-day basis. This does not alter the dutyholder's legal responsibility for the health and safety of everyone on the installation. This means that the OIM will need to ensure that all relevant legislation has been complied with - including LOLER and PUWER. MAR requires everyone on the installation to co-operate with the OIM. So, for example, contractors' employees engaged in crane maintenance will need to make their risk assessments available to the OIM and to others such as employees of other specialist contract firms who may be affected by their work.

12   There are links between LOLER, PUWER and the Management of Health and Safety at Work Regulations 1999 (MHSWR).[10] For example, regulation 3 of MHSWR requires a suitable and sufficient risk assessment to be performed for all work activity. This only requires a single risk assessment, which should be carried out by a competent person(s).

13   Throughout this guidance, frequent references are made to the 'competent person'. In this context, the 'competent person' is the most suitable person or persons to agree and implement the recommendations in this guidance. The competent person(s) may be employed by the dutyholder, contractors, verification bodies, a manufacturer, supplier or agent etc. They should have the necessary training, background and experience to be recognised as being competent in the particular field in which they specialise. It is highly unlikely that any one person - or even organisation - will be able to provide all the areas of expertise required throughout this guidance. Instead, a number of people or organisations would be involved.

14   When new legislation is introduced, unless specified in the associated statutory instrument, there is normally no requirement for new provisions to apply retrospectively. However, there are general requirements for employers to ensure, so far as is reasonably practicable, the health and safety of all employees at work. This duty covers the equipment provided, its maintenance and the systems of work that are used. In discharging these responsibilities, the employer has to take account of new technology and innovations, and the greater reliability or effectiveness that may be provided by new equipment. The greater the risks (for example, risks that occur during man-riding or lifting over live processing plants or well heads) then it is more likely that it is reasonable to go to very substantial expense, trouble and invention to reduce these risks. It is important that employers and their appointed competent persons are continually checking to ensure that old and existing lifting equipment is suitable and fit for purpose and does not pose any increased risk during operations. This is the requirement under the HSW Act.

15   While employees do not have duties under LOLER, they do have general duties under the HSW Act and MHSWR to take reasonable care of themselves and others who may be affected by their actions and to co-operate with others.

Technical guidance on the safe use of lifting equipment offshore

General considerations

Selecting suitable equipment

16   You should select lifting equipment which is suitable for the operations it will be required to perform. You should base your final selection on a risk assessment of the proposed use of the equipment. Before starting to use them, the dutyholder and the competent person should satisfy themselves that lifting appliances and any associated equipment have been designed, manufactured and verified fit for purpose in accordance with recognised codes and standards applicable to the offshore industry.

Risk assessment

17   The risk assessment should include, as a minimum:

■   an analysis of failure modes and their consequential effects;
■   personnel protection requirements;
■   effects of abnormal situations, eg gross overloading;
■   emergency procedures for recovering loads or personnel; and
■   human factors.

18   If a lifting system is to be adapted for a new operation (different from the one it was first installed for), or if it is to be moved to a new location, then it will need a full risk assessment covering its intended new use. This should be approved by a competent person.

19   There are particular factors in the offshore environment which you should consider when assessing both the technical and operational aspects of lifting and handling tasks. You should incorporate these into the risk assessment, together with any special factors such as use of the equipment in explosive atmospheres.

Details of service

20   You may need to discuss the suitability of lifting equipment with the supplier. You will also need to provide details of service. You will need to consider the factors below when deciding the correct equipment for a particular task:

■   maximum sea state;
■   maximum wind velocity;
■   maximum and minimum ambient temperatures;
■   snow/ice build-up;
■   immersion in sea water;
■   supply vessel excursion;
■   movements of the installation/vessel, ie heel, trim and pitch; and
■   exposure to chemicals and other hazardous substances.

21   You will also need to consider how often the lifting equipment will be used and advise the supplier of any regular periods of inactivity or extended periods of non-use. If you need a mobile crane, you should also tell the supplier whether it will need to operate free on tracks or wheels, fixed or tied down or travelling with the load.

Specifications

22   The competent person (see paragraph 13) should ensure, as far as is practicable, that the equipment supplied:

■   has been manufactured from suitable materials and constructed to approved quality standards;
■   has adequate safety factors;
■   has adequate levels of performance; and
■   where appropriate has responsive controls and safety systems.

23   For slewing cranes which perform sea-state lifting, a competent person selected by the dutyholder should ensure that the crane has adequate hoist speed and power to perform correctly in all modes of operation. Low hoist speeds may restrict the number of falls of rope that can be used for a particular sea state and so limit the lifting capacity of the crane. It is essential to prevent risks and hazards arising from the under-performance of cranes. The competent person should ensure that the following aspects of crane performance are considered:

■   The hook speed should be fast enough for the specified sea states to prevent the load re-impacting with the supply vessel. The height of adjacent containers on the deck of the supply vessel should be taken into account.
■   The speed of slew, boom and hoist motion should be fast enough for the operator to keep the hook/load line sensibly plumb within the excursion envelope of the supply vessel and within the specified offlead and sidelead parameters.
■   Using two or more crane services should not cause undesirable motions of the hook/load.
■   The prime mover should be prevented from stalling or over-heating under maximum power demand, whatever the configuration of the crane.
■   Uncontrolled overhauling and/or free fall of the load hoist and boom hoist system and uncontrolled slewing motion of the crane are dangerous and should be prevented.

24   However, some cranes may incorporate emergency release devices to prevent gross overloads (for example arising from a snagged hook/load), and when these are actuated they may automatically override some of the features listed above. All emergency release devices should be made inactive every time the load travels across areas of the installation.

25   For slewing cranes (pedestal or mobile), lifting duty charts - including environmental and/or operational limitations - should be clearly and permanently displayed at the operator's control station and be included in the operational manual. For cranes that undertake sea-state lifting, the duty charts should have reduced lifting capacities appropriate to dynamic factors for the prevailing sea state. These should be agreed by a competent person. A suitable rated capacity indicator (RCI) should be fitted that covers all duty ratings the crane will be subjected to, for both inboard and sea-state lifting operations. It should be possible, either manually or automatically, to change the load rating of the

crane in accordance with the sea-state/inboard lifting duty charts.

26   As appropriate to the type of lifting equipment (and as required), you should provide lifting duty/rating charts according to the service parameters. These charts should be drawn up using recognised de-rating methods and procedures, such as laid down in codes of practice issued by the various verification bodies. Dynamic factors should be based on information obtained from standards and codes used for the design and component selection for the crane.

27   You should ensure that for beam cranes, gantry cranes, trolley hoists or any equipment that can lift and/or travel the load, the travelling system remains captive to its rails and/or its points of attachment. The load should remain captive to its hook or attachment point under all conditions of service.

28   When using rope/chain hoists, the evaluation of loading in the supporting structure, such as runway beams, trolleys, pad eyes etc, should include:

■   the load on the hook;
■   the weight of slings and attachments;
■   the weight of the hoist unit/trolley; and
■   as appropriate, the pulling force on the hand chain.

For routine lifts this only needs to be carried out on an initial basis and re-evaluated only for non-routine operations.

29   Loose accessories for lifting, such as strops, slings, pennants and spreader beams, should be supplied with suitable documentation stating that they have been tested, inspected and verified as being fit for purpose. See also paragraphs 52-55.

Material selection

30   Materials used in the primary load path (including foundations and both permanent and temporary attachment points) should be chosen according to recognised standards and to the specific requirements and limitations agreed with the competent person.

31   Material certificates for all primary elements, including castings and forgings, should provide details of all necessary chemical and mechanical properties, including fracture toughness values at specified low temperature conditions where appropriate. Mechanical properties of materials should be quoted after any heat treatment which may have altered the original properties. It is perfectly acceptable to use test coupons to obtain these properties, provided they have been subjected to the same heat treatment process as the original material. For loose gear and accessories, a certificate of conformity for primary load-carrying elements should be provided. This should be kept up to date and be available at a readily accessible location (see paragraph 52) for as long as the equipment is used at the work site.

32   Where, because of the age of the equipment, material records and specifications are not available, a risk

assessment should be carried out which enables the competent person to assess whether the equipment is suitable for its defined duty and its operation in specified environmental conditions.

Welding

33   Weld design for primary load-bearing structures should conform to recognised codes and standards. Allowance should be made for dynamic stress, load spectra and fatigue resistance. You may need to consider the need for redundancy on certain structural and mechanical elements.

34   Welding and welded repairs should be undertaken by suitably qualified welders to agreed specified procedures. These should be appropriate to the materials involved and to the type and configuration of the weld. Any heat treatment after welding must be carried out to recognised procedures agreed between you and the competent person. Any repairs and modifications should not degrade or alter the performance of the lifting equipment. However, if this cannot be guaranteed, then suitable amended load ratings should be calculated by the competent person and the equipment re-marked accordingly.

35   Where practicable and feasible, welding for all primary and secondary steelworks should be continuous on each side of the joint to safeguard against crevice corrosion. You should consider using sealing welds and closure plates for box section fabrications to safeguard against crevice corrosion.

Corrosion protection

36   Corrosive oxides can build up extremely quickly on ferrous materials used in a saline environment. This corrosive development may be accelerated where higher temperatures are involved, eg from external sources such as flares or turbine exhaust or from internal sources such as diesel prime movers and hydraulic systems. Where possible, you should specify components from non-corrosive materials, particularly for components which are critical to the safe operation and control of the lifting equipment. If this is not possible, you should apply suitable corrosion protection methods.

37   Safety-critical fasteners, such as slewbearing fasteners, should be suitably protected against corrosion, eg by using grease-filled shrouds. Fasteners used for other critical principal joint connections should also be suitably protected against corrosion. If chemical coatings are used for protection purposes (galvanised, sheradised, cadmium coating etc) then care should be taken that galvanic action between the fastener coating and the surrounding material does not occur.

38   Paint specifications that provide protection against corrosion should be of a type suitable for use in an offshore environment.

39   Electrical, pneumatic and hydraulic components and systems should be evaluated for use in a saline

environment. Note that these systems, when used on mobile cranes, will usually be based on automotive product standards and may not be suitable for offshore use.

Access and escape

40 You should ensure that there are safe methods of access and escape for everyone working on or near lifting equipment. This applies to its regular operation or to facilitate tasks such as maintenance. Access ways, exit ways and escape routes provided for general use on the installation should not be obstructed or in any way compromised when operating, maintaining, erecting or dismantling the equipment.

41 Access ways should not require operators to work directly under the load or allow the load to pass directly over others on the installation.

42 Major lifting equipment such as slewing cranes (fixed and mobile) should incorporate access ways to the control station or to the operator's compartment. To enable routine checks and maintenance to be effectively undertaken in slewing cranes, you should consider providing access ways (preferably built-in) to:

■ the boom head;
■ the length of the boom;
■ the A-frame apex;
■ the interior of the pedestal (fixed cranes);
■ the machinery house; and
■ all winch/drum systems.

43 The surfaces of flat area access ways, for example machinery house roofs, should be non-slip - chequer plate or similar - and be enclosed by steel handrails. Where necessary, they should incorporate self-closing and self-latching gates.

44 The location of all access ways should allow people to leave the area regardless of the position or configuration of the crane. Where access ways are located 2 metres or more above the deck of the installation, you should consider providing suitable fixings for safety harnesses to be used.

45 You should agree with the competent person any temporary access ways, ladders, scaling boards etc. Installation and dismantling of temporary access equipment should be carried out by people who are competent and experienced at these tasks.

46 Fixed (permanent) ladders should be constructed to recognised codes and standards. Safety hoops and intermittent landings when required should comply with all the necessary industry requirements.

Inspection

47 Lifting equipment and accessories, together with foundation, anchor and attachment points, will all need to be covered by a thorough examination scheme. The written scheme should take account of the following:

■ exposure to environmental conditions, heat sources, extreme low temperatures and moisture;
■ materials and construction of the equipment that may give rise to the development of corrosion or failure from abrasion (as may happen in wire ropes and the internals of structural hollow sections);
■ effects of dynamic loading and out-of-plumb forces;
■ the duty cycle - frequency of use or extended periods of idleness or storage;
■ repetitive working of the equipment which may cause localised wear in key components;
■ the condition of primary structures, fixings, components, brakes, control and safety systems;
■ the condition and security of access ways, escape routes and escape systems that may be incorporated, for example as part of crane or drilling equipment; and
■ repairs or modifications to primary load-carrying structural elements or component parts, and any changes that may affect the performance of the lifting appliance or its limitations of use.

48 In circumstances where equipment may have been subject to undue overloading during operation (not test loading), all primary safety-critical load path structures should be thoroughly examined and documented by a competent person. This should include mountings, fixings, components, brakes, safety devices and any accessory used in the lifting equipment system. This examination may require checks for damaged screw threads of fasteners, and deformation, permanent set or dimensional changes in key components when referenced to the original engineering drawings. Any remedial work to restore the lifting equipment to its original specification should be approved and documented by a competent person. The cause of any undue overloading of lifting equipment in service should be documented and validated by the competent person. It may be necessary to examine any load data that is available, for example from load monitoring/recording systems from cranes and drilling equipment.

49 The intervals between thorough examinations will depend on a risk assessment based on the type of lifting equipment, its location, and how it is intended to be used. Inspections may range from visual inspection to a detailed thorough examination. This may include testing using suitable techniques considered appropriate by a competent person of independent standing, ie who can exercise impartial judgement.

50 When thorough examinations are required, you may carry this out either according to a specified period approach (as specified by LOLER) or by a written examination scheme drawn up by the competent person. If you choose not to produce a written examination scheme, you will need to follow a specified period approach as laid down by LOLER.

51 Your thorough examination procedures should include all known environmental and operational factors, including any factors which could adversely affect the lifting equipment, such as:

- undue exposure to environmental conditions;
- sub-sea operations;
- sub-zero or elevated ambient temperatures;
- corrosion effects;
- ingress of moisture; or
- extended periods of idleness or infrequent use.

Documentation, reports and test details

52   You will need to consider how and where you store all documentation relating to lifting equipment, so that people such as contractors, maintenance staff and competent persons can refer to it easily. You will also need to bear in mind the need to keep the documents up to date and that they reflect the 'as currently operated' status of the specific equipment and systems on the installation. You need to ensure that your system includes documentation relating to mobile equipment which can be moved from one location to another.

53   As a general guide, the minimum up-to-date documentation available should be:

- operation and maintenance manuals;
- the risk assessment analysis;
- records of inspection/thorough examination reports (Note: reports of thorough examinations should contain all the information specified in Schedule 1 of LOLER);
- records of any major safety-critical component which has been replaced (cranes only); and
- details of any report by a competent person which has been made under regulation 10(c) of LOLER.

54   Documents should be available which demonstrate that the lifting equipment or system is fit for purpose and safe for use according to the prescribed duties and limitations of use. Details of the design and testing (including any overload testing) should be included. Some examples of equipment requiring this documentation are:

- hook block assemblies, wire ropes and loose gear (slings etc);
- safety systems, including gross overload protection (GOP) systems;
- electrical equipment and diesel engines used in potentially explosive atmospheres;
- slewbearings and slewbearing fasteners; and
- foundations, padeyes, anchor point attachments, runway beams etc.

55   Where type testing has been employed, for example, for hook block assemblies, and where only a percentage of the equipment has been physically subjected to an overload test, this should be clearly stated in the associated documentation.

Testing

56   Testing of new or substantially repaired or modified lifting equipment, foundations, fixings, lifting points etc should be agreed by the equipment supplier and a competent person appropriate to the type of lifting equipment.

57   Weights used for load/overload testing should be marked in accordance with the details of a calibration certificate, provided by a competent person, which shows the proven accuracy of the weight(s). When water weights are used, the potential loss of containment of large volumes of water, the movement of water in semi-filled bags, and the consequential effects should be carefully evaluated.

58   When load/overload testing lifting equipment, a competent person should ensure that:

- the lifting equipment is thoroughly examined before testing;
- the test load does not exceed the limits specified by the equipment supplier;
- each primary mechanical and structural element is subjected to the test load;
- test loads are kept as near to the deck or floor as possible;
- the deck or floor area can adequately support the test load;
- the environmental conditions are suitable (when testing offshore);
- the test area is effectively enclosed and warning notices are posted;
- the lifting equipment is thoroughly examined after the test; and
- details of the test, including any deficiencies arising, are documented and corrective action instigated where necessary.

Operation

Planning the use of lifting equipment

59   You should plan each lifting operation to ensure the lifting equipment and the load remain stable throughout the lifting operation.

60   When planning the use of lifting equipment, you should identify the controls necessary to eliminate or control the associated risks. Some relevant factors are:

- fences and collision-prevention barriers to protect sensitive plant and equipment;
- at least one unobstructed route of access and escape for people operating the lifting equipment;
- environmental factors which may influence the design, safe use and safe securing of the lifting equipment, including:
    - maximum operational wind speed;
    - storm wind speed;
    - maximum sea state;
    - maximum and minimum air temperatures; and
    - loading caused by snow and ice build-up.
- the effects of incident heat from flare systems, gas turbine exhausts or any other heat source. Workers should not be exposed to elevated temperatures caused by these;
- dynamic factors arising from the movements of the installation, attendant vessels etc;

■ measures to prevent:
- uncontrolled movement of the equipment and load;
- overloading;
- snagging;
- spillage of load contents;
- collision;
- the load from dropping;
- failure of equipment, foundations and fixing;

■ how to prevent movement of the lifting equipment and the load during the changeover between working shifts;

■ effective security of the lifting equipment when out of use during storms and during sea transit of mobile installations, vessels or ships; and

■ for mobile cranes, identified dedicated lifting areas on the installation. A competent person should approve the suitability and strength of these lifting areas.

61   Where mats, beams or timbers are used for distributing the load of mobile cranes that travel across the installation, these should be securely fixed to the installation's structure in a manner approved by a competent person (see paragraph 101).

62   The written procedures for the planned lifting operation should also specify:

■ the validation of the weight of the load (including the weight of containers and/or any ancillary attachments), its centre of gravity and method of securing against unintentional movement during the lifting operation;

■ the validation and documentation of the capacity and factors of safety of lifting equipment, slings, attachments, foundations etc (determined by test and/or by calculation appropriate to the type of lifting equipment);

■ the strength and space of laydown areas, and clearances between the load and the lifting appliance, structural elements and plant and equipment;

■ any changes in the distribution of the load or the lifting appliance such as the dynamic effects arising from environmental factors or from the transfer of the load from one lifting appliance to another (see paragraph 63);

■ the handling of dangerous or hazardous materials, such as drilling chemicals;

■ procedures for erecting and dismantling the lifting equipment;

■ procedures for safe release of sea fastenings;

■ identification of restricted areas;

■ the proximity of other people working in the vicinity of the moving load;

■ as appropriate to floating installations or vessels:
- the trim of the installation/vessel throughout the lifting operation;
- the necessary response of the dynamic positioning system;
- the adequate bedding of anchors, where these are deployed;
- the tension in the mooring tethers/lines and procedures for keeping these within controlled limits; and

■ procedures for stopping or abandoning the lifting operation which may be necessary due to environmental factors, overload, failure of the lifting system or human factors.

63   The combined use of more than one item of lifting equipment should be assessed, planned and supervised by a competent person.

64   When using multiple chain hoist systems, each individual hoist unit should be rated to a capacity of at least 100% of the load. You should plan the use of multiple hoists and any operation involving the transfer of the load from one hoist to another using clearly defined procedures relevant to each event of the lifting operation. You should consider using drawings or sketches in support of the procedures.

Safe system of work

65   You should ensure all lifting operations are carried out in accordance with a written safe system of work (SSW). This should include instructions on how to eliminate or adequately control risks identified in the equipment assessment. This philosophy should be applied to both routine and specialised operations. Procedures for routine lifting operations, such as loading and backloading containers from the supply vessel, should be kept under review to ensure they remain valid.

66   The SSW should identify control procedures needed. It should address the following:

■ planning the lifting operation (see paragraphs 59-64);
■ the results of any risk assessment on the operation and equipment (see paragraphs 17-19); and
■ the issue and authorisation of work permits.

67   Procedures should include the following:

■ The following checks should be carried out:
- all equipment should be examined prior to use;
- all loose equipment should have a valid report of thorough examination by a competent person and/or a suitable declaration of conformity;
- pre-start checks should be provided by the equipment supplier or the competent person; and
- all equipment should be in a good state of repair before being stored.

■ Everyone involved with mechanical handling operations should be trained to a level of competence appropriate to their tasks and responsibilities.

■ No-one should work under a suspended load and no load should pass over people.

■ There should be an effective system for reporting and recording any incident arising from the operational use or from failure of the lifting or mechanical handling equipment.

■ A clear and effective communication system should be available and understood by everyone involved with the lifting operation.

■ A competent person should be identified to co-ordinate and control all aspects of the lifting operation.

■ A shift change-over scheme should be in place which

correctly informs the incoming shift of anything in the lifting operation or lifting equipment which may affect the safe operation of cranes or other lifting equipment. This means notifying any change in circumstances which may require alteration to the system of work, eg moving the drilling derrick to a new well slot or changes to scaffolding.

■ Adequate lighting and effective unobstructed access ways and escape routes should be provided and maintained (see paragraphs 40-46).

Operating the equipment

68   For all types of lifting equipment, you should ensure that:

■ uncontrolled movements of the equipment and load are prevented;
■ brakes and control systems are 'fail-safe';
■ brakes hold the load, including test load, indefinitely without slip;
■ power driving through applied brakes is not possible (unless for the purpose of testing);
■ over-hauling or overspeeding of the equipment by the load is prevented;
■ all motion of the equipment and the load are effectively arrested in the event of power loss or system failure and that, under these conditions, provision is made to recover the equipment and load to a safe location.

69   Dutyholders, contractors and everyone using or working with lifting equipment should ensure that the equipment is not misused, does not operate outside its defined duties and is not loaded beyond its operational limitations.

70   The storage, inspection, maintenance etc of lifting accessories (slings, shackles etc) and of portable lifting machines such as hand chain hoists and lever pulls should be controlled by a suitable system, for example the 'lifting loft' procedure.

71   BS 7121 Part 11[11] contains much useful information on the operation and use of cranes offshore.

72   Manual chain hoists may be used for lifting or moving a single load. These hoist units, unlike a crane, do not incorporate any form of safe load indicator, so the load carried by each individual hoist unit (in a multiple hoist set-up) will be unknown. These loads can, even under the most resolute control and co-ordination, vary considerably from zero on one or two hoists to one carrying 100% of the load. When transferring the load from one hoist to another, the angle made by the chain may overload the hoist unit or cause the load or the hoist/beam/trolley to move uncontrollably.

73   When more than one hoist is used to lift a single load, for example on a blow-out preventer (BOP) crane that may use two hoist units to lift the BOP, you should ensure that the loads in each hoist line remain fully equalised throughout the operation, by using either a load-compensating sheave/block or a load sensor/indicator system.

Operations in potentially explosive atmospheres

74   The selection, operation and maintenance of all lifting equipment for use in potentially explosive atmospheres needs careful consideration. You should also consider all electrical and relevant mechanical components which need to comply with the relevant legislation, standards and codes of practice. Examples are:

■ the need for flameproofing diesel engines;
■ the use of fire resistant lubricating oils and greases;
■ means of reducing incendive sparking;
■ control of surface temperatures; and
■ the use of certified electrical apparatus for the predicted explosive atmosphere.

75   You should identify the level of protection required and inform the lifting equipment supplier. You will need to inform the competent person in making this decision.

76   For all diesel-driven cranes used in potentially explosive atmospheres, you should consider using air or hydraulic start systems supplied either directly from the crane or via a local plug-in supply from the installation. Battery, glow plug or alcohol-aided start systems are not recommended. If batteries are used, a double pole isolation switch should be provided as close to the battery terminals as possible.

77   Travelling, steering or spragging crawler-type cranes over a steel deck or steel bearers may generate unacceptable levels of sparking and, if used in potentially explosive atmospheres, you will need to take appropriate measures to prevent this.

Marking equipment

78   You, or a delegated competent person, should ensure that all lifting equipment (including accessories) is clearly and permanently marked to identify the equipment and to indicate its safe working load (SWL) (also known as rated load or working load limit). You should use a method of marking that does not, of itself, raise stress levels in the equipment and will not become damaged by operating the equipment. Marking on pedestal cranes, mobile cranes, overhead travelling cranes, gantry cranes, runway beams, padeyes etc should be clearly visible to people operating the equipment or working nearby.

79   The SWL may vary with changes in configuration or geometry of the lifting equipment, for example with pedestal and mobile type cranes. In this case, the crane should be clearly marked so that its maximum SWL (as applied to inboard lifting duties) relates both to minimum and maximum operating radius, length of boom and the number of falls of rope used in the hoist system. As well as these maximum ratings, the crane's derated duties for dynamic lifting operations appropriate to specified sea states should be permanently indicated in the crane operator's compartment or control station, together with any other limitations of use. The full range of crane duties for inboard and outboard lifting should be included in the crane operating manual and be loaded in the crane's rated capacity indicator (RCI) system.

80   Where strops, sling sets etc are used, the marking of the SWL should also relate to the working angle of the strop or sling. Where a colour coding system is used to identify the suitability of equipment for a particular use, this should be clearly indicated in the written procedures.

81   Lifting equipment, attachments and fixings which are not marked or which do not identify with an in-date test document should not be used until these requirements are checked and validated by a competent person.

82   Where required by regulation, you should ensure that lifting equipment either:

■   carries the appropriate CE mark; or
■   satisfies essential health and safety requirements.

Note that a CE mark does not guarantee that the equipment or system is fit for purpose.

Training

83   You should ensure that people using or in any way responsible for the operating or maintenance of lifting equipment receive adequate training. This should be relevant to their tasks and responsibilities and the type of lifting equipment used. Training should be aimed at achieving levels of competence that will minimise the potential for human error or behaviour which might cause an accident. To do this, the training may need to include:

■   the results of any risk assessment appropriate to the task;
■   the results of any examination of the equipment in use;
■   any preventative measure implemented as a result of previous incidents; and
■   any special arrangements such as safe systems of work.

84   People being trained should only undertake tasks according to their assessed level of competence, and only under the supervision of a qualified person.

85   Training should ensure that everyone engaged in lifting operations fully understands the roles and responsibilities of others involved. It should ensure that interactions of riggers, slingers, load handlers, crane operators, supply vessel crew etc are co-ordinated and are directed solely by a competent person.

86   Operators should be familiar with any sensitivities and limitations of the lifting equipment and of any restrictions or special procedures for its safe use. For example, where a lifting operation may obscure the crane operator's view of the hook or load, then the banksman/slinger should be positioned to fully sight the hook/load so they can give effective directions to the crane operator.

87   Operators should be qualified to ensure that:

■   the lifting equipment, or any part, such as slings and spreaders, identifies with an in-date document

(provided by a competent person after thorough examination within the regulatory period) validating that the equipment is fit for purpose;
■   the lifting equipment is visually checked for defects/damage prior to use;
■   all limitations of use, including any required derating of the equipment, are observed;
■   all operating procedures, including test procedures, are observed; and
■   in the event of power failure or overload, the load and the lifting equipment are made safe.

88   The people who are likely to need training in the safe operation of lifting equipment are:

■   crane operators;
■   banksmen and signallers;
■   riggers and users of portable lifting equipment (including manual or powered hoists etc);
■   slingers and load handlers; and
■   maintenance and inspection personnel.

89   You should check the continued competence of these people regularly. You will need to document your arrangements for doing this.

90   People who are primarily involved with other tasks, such as production or drilling operations, but who may also be required to perform lifting duties or maintain lifting equipment, should also be adequately trained.

91   People involved in erecting and dismantling mechanical handling equipment should be adequately trained and experienced in this work.

Types of offshore lifting equipment

Cranes - variable geometry slewing types

Introduction

92   Variable geometry slewing cranes, including fixed pedestal cranes and mobile cranes (tracked or wheel mounted), that operate in fixed or travelling mode should follow the appropriate recommendations of this section in order to meet the stability requirements of regulation 4 of PUWER.

93   Mobile cranes are particularly sensitive to external influences such as environmental effects, installation movements, and dynamic loading. A competent person should assess the suitability of a mobile crane for use offshore according to service requirements, type of installation, location and operational risk assessment.

94   For offshore use, mobile cranes and fixed pedestal-type cranes that feature all-hydraulic power transmission, integrated control systems, enclosed gear drives and brakes are preferable to mechanically-driven cranes using open gear drives and open brakes/clutches. If mobile cranes operate in tied-down or fixed mode, the lifting duties may change from a regime based largely on stability to a regime limited wholly by structural and/or component strength.

95   All mobile cranes should be fitted with an approved Rated Capacity Indicator (RCI). Where sea lifts are to be undertaken, the RCI should incorporate de-rating curves for the sea-state in which it will be operating.

96   Table 1 shows, in general terms, the suitability of various types of mobile crane for use offshore.

97   You should also consider the following when selecting mobile cranes for use offshore:

■   Cranes which travel/carry the load free on tyres should be safeguarded against tyre burst - consider using solid tyres.
■   Cranes which operate with outriggers deployed should be designed to withstand any high pressure generated in the outrigger hydraulic system by dynamic lifting operations.
■   Booms should have adequate torsional stiffness, rigidity and lateral stability for the specified service. It is particularly important to assess box section booms of the type used on ram luffing/telescoping cranes for suitability.
■   Because of the particularly large and random motions of tension legged platforms, semi-submersibles and monohull vessels arising from wave action, travelling or free-standing mobile cranes are not recommended. This does not apply to crane barges, which are inherently more stable than other types of monohull vessels.

TYPE OF MOBILE CRANE AND MODE OF USE	INSTALLATION TYPE					
	Fixed		Semi-sub		Monohull	
	Sea lifts	Inboard lifts	Sea lifts	Inboard lifts	Sea lifts	Inboard lifts
Wheelmount - free lifting/ travelling on tyres	NR	POSS	NR	POSS	NR	NR
Wheelmount - free on outriggers	POSS	YES	POSS	POSS	NR	NR
Wheelmount - outriggers tied-down	YES	YES	YES	YES	POSS	POSS
Wheelmount - fixed/tied-down chassis	YES	YES	YES	YES	POSS	POSS
Crawler crane - free lifting/ travelling on tracks	YES	YES	YES	YES	NR	NR
Crawler crane - tied-down	YES	YES	YES	YES	YES	YES
Crawler crane without travel facility - tied-down	YES	YES	YES	YES	YES	YES

NR   - Not recommended
POSS- Possible option, which should be fully assessed by a competent person
YES   - Preferred option but should be assessed by a competent person

Table 1 Suitability of mobile cranes for use offshore

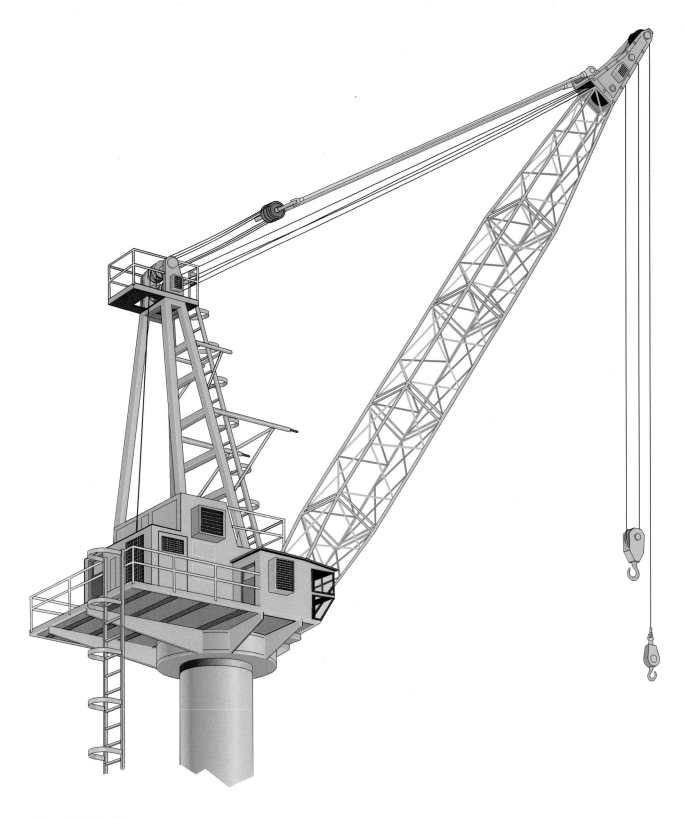

Figure 1 Pedestal crane

Mobile cranes travelling with load

Design

98   The deck structure of the installation and any mats or bearers should be designed to support all forces generated by the operation and test loading of the crane, including:

■   the maximum force that may cause the crane to tip at one end roller of a crawler crane, at one wheel of a wheel-mounted crane or at one outrigger/jack of a wheel-mounted crane;

■   tractive forces, ie forces to propel/travel the crane;

■   braking forces when arresting travelling or slewing, and when decelerating the load hoist and boom;

■   dynamic forces, including any forces arising from offleads/sideleads;

15

- forces generated by steering/spragging of the crane; and
- forces induced by any motion of the installation or vessel.

Selecting suitable equipment

99   Where cranes are required to travel with the load, particularly on mobile installations, the motion of the vessel may cause the load to pendulum and adversely affect the stability of the crane. A competent person should carefully consider this. On wheel-mounted cranes, the effects of tyre floatation will add to the pendulum problem. Wheel-mounted cranes would not normally be considered suitable for travelling with the load on mobile floating installations. See also paragraphs 16-29 *(Selecting suitable equipment)* and 59-64 *(Planning the use of lifting equipment)*.

Figure 2 Crawler crane

Operation

100 You should inform the competent person when planning to use mobile cranes on a temporary basis. You should also inform them of the operational duties and length of time that the mobile crane will be used.

101 The competent person should ensure that all forces and ground pressures transmitted to the installation deck have been fully assessed. They should also consider carefully the potential fire risk and trip hazards when assessing the use of timber baulks as bearers. Mats and bearers used to spread these forces should be positively and effectively secured to the deck of the installation. They should not deviate, move, spread or cause any de-stabilising effects during the lifting operation.

102 Mats or bearers should be level and should not be contaminated by any substance (including oil or grease) which would cause the crane to skid or slip. Contaminants may increase their combustible potential.

Mobile cranes tied-down - deck loading

103 Mobile cranes may be required to operate in tied down or fixed mode at dedicated locations on an installation. In this case, the location of the fixing points on the crane and the method of fixing (by welding, bolting, turnbuckles etc) should be agreed between the competent person and the crane manufacturer or supplier.

104 The crane manufacturer or supplier should provide details of all forces transmitted to the installation structure arising from the operational service parameters notified by the competent person. The competent person should provide an assessment of the strength and failure mode sequence of the fixing points and of the crane's primary load path elements. These should include, as appropriate:

- boom;
- A-frame;
- gantry mast;
- bedplate;
- carbody;
- chassis;
- outriggers;
- hydraulic rams (luffing, telescoping and outriggers);
- slewbearing and fasteners; and
- all primary load carrying pins.

The sequence of failure should be such that the tie-down/fixings are the last to fail.

Braking systems

105 For normal crane operations, when power-lowering the load hoist and boom hoist motions, dynamic braking or retardation of the crane motions should be effected through the crane's transmission system. A friction-type brake or brakes should also be provided, with adequate redundancy, to prevent:

- free-fall of the boom;
- free-fall of the hook load; or
- free slewing.

Design

106 Brakes should be spring-applied and should fully engage when the controller is released and automatically returns to its spring-centred neutral position, brakes should also fully automatically engage if there is a loss of power in the transmission and/or control system. They should be designed to hold indefinitely without slip. The braking system should provide for the controlled lowering of the boom and hook load, and for recovering the crane to a safe location on the installation if there is a major failure of transmission system or power loss to the crane. Under these circumstances, the brakes should be rated for dynamic operation.

Selecting suitable equipment

107 For winch drums, it is preferable for at least one brake to act directly on the drum or as near to the drum as is practicable. For wheel-mounted mobile cranes, travel brakes should act directly at the wheels. If brakes are located at the low torque drive end of a gearbox, downstream of a winch drum or the wheels of a mobile crane, all driving elements of the gearbox and transmission system should be rated to at least the torque holding capacity of the brake(s).

108 Brakes should be fully protected against the environment and other contaminants.

Winch drums and sheaves

109 Rope life, particularly in terms of bending fatigue, is greatly influenced by the diameter of the winch drums or sheaves. The pitch diameter of drums and sheaves should be as large as practicable and should not be less than the minimum required by the relevant standards and/or the requirements specified by the rope manufacturer or supplier.

110 Drums should be grooved or incorporate grooved laggings. The number of layers of rope spooled should be as low as possible. Ropes should be spooled onto drums in a controlled manner, ensuring that specified fleet angles are maintained throughout their working travel for all configurations of the crane. A minimum of three turns of rope should remain on the drum under all operating circumstances and also for the safe stowage of the crane. Where a secondary tailing rope is fitted, this should not compromise the spooling of the primary rope.

111 There should be means to ensure that ropes remain captive to the drums and sheaves at all times, particularly when there is low tension in the rope. Drum capacities should be such that when the rope is fully spooled onto the drum, there is adequate height between the top rope layer and the top of the drum flange to prevent the rope slipping over the flange.

112   The competent person should assess drum assemblies and their fixing to the crane. They should consider:

- the maximum rope tension arising from dynamic loading conditions, frictional and environmental effects;
- the maximum force generated during a static overload test; and
- the forces generated under gross overload situations which may occur with the hook or load snagging with a supply vessel.

113   The competent person should consider the effect of plastic sheaves, especially with respect to the fatigue life and wear characteristics of wire ropes. They should look out for enhanced fatigue wear on ropes, especially when plastic and steel sheave combinations are fitted to cranes.

Wire rope and terminations

Wire rope

114   You should select wire ropes and pendants in accordance with recognised standards and with due regard to their intended service. Wire ropes should be manufactured in a single uninterrupted continuous length. Increasing the length by splicing or other methods is not an acceptable practice. You should ensure that the grooving of sheaves and drums used in the system is compatible with the selected rope.

115   Ropes other than those originally specified should not be used without the approval of a competent person.

116   A competent person should specify a wire rope replacement policy, both for standing and running ropes. This policy should include:

- the intervals between inspection/service checks and discard/replacement criteria;
- details of removal for examination and servicing prior to replacement;
- destructive proof testing of representative rope and appropriate non-destructive testing (NDT) of the full length of the installed rope if the rope is to be re-used;
- procedures for any change or replacement of the rope from that originally specified;
- lubrication proposals, which should include details of lubrication prior to the rope being placed into service offshore, and intervals of re-lubrication according to rope type and operational service. High-pressure lubrication systems should be used for this purpose.

117   You should maintain a record of all wire ropes fitted to a crane. Records should include:

- the manufacturer's certificate validating the rope's mechanical properties in accordance with a recognised standard;
- validation of testing;

- the date the rope was fitted;
- previous periods of service; and
- any maintenance or repair work carried out on the rope.

Further recommendations on wire ropes are in BS 7121 Part 11[11] and also BS EN 12385: 2000.[12]

Terminations

118   Rope terminations and anchorages at drums should preferably be made outside the drum flanges and in a manner that facilitates ready inspection. Special anchor arrangements may be needed for hoist ropes with a tailing rope (see paragraph 110).

119   All other rope end terminations should be made in accordance with recognised standards, eg BS EN 13411-3: 2004.[13] Any thimbles should comply with recognised standards and be compatible with the diameter and breaking load of the rope. Solid thimbles are recommended. Spliced terminations may be used with the appropriate thimble, provided the splicing is to proven standards.

120   It is not recommended to use wire rope grips for terminations on any rope used in the crane's primary load path. Grips may be used to tie back the free end of the rope on wedge and socket terminations. The correct fitting and tightening of wire rope grips should be approved by a competent person.

121   Any load testing required to prove the integrity of the termination should be carried out or witnessed by a competent person and appropriately documented.

122   You should keep a record of all rope anchorages and terminations and should include details of any changes or replacements. Terminations and anchorages should not be replaced with other types without the approval of a competent person. Steel sockets should be suitable for the environmental conditions and shock loadings they may be subjected to in service.

123   The dutyholder's records should show the efficiency of end terminations. These should be agreed with the competent person and approved by an independent verification body for the equipment in question.

Operator's control compartment or stand

Selecting suitable equipment

124   The findings of a risk assessment should determine the location and protection arrangements for the operator's control compartment or stand. This assessment should consider how to protect the operator from falling objects (including parts of the crane), swinging loads, environmental conditions and any elevated temperatures. If protection is considered to be unnecessary, the reasoning should be stated. Control compartments or stands which may be located in a potentially explosive atmosphere should be protected in accordance with paragraphs 74-77.

125   When the compartment or stand is located on the crane's slewing structure, the operator should have a clear view of the hook throughout the crane's full slewing circle and an unobstructed line of sight from boom tip to the deck of a supply vessel. If this is not possible, you should have procedures to ensure the motions of the crane are safely directed. For mobile cranes, compartments should ensure effective rearward as well as forward viewing. Compartments or stands which are remote from the crane's structure should be assessed and approved by a competent person.

126   The compartment or stand should be provided with safe access and escape routes under all operating conditions and configurations of the crane and for any maintenance or repair work.

Operation

127   High-pressure hoses should not be located in the compartment, unless needed for controls and instrumentation. In these cases, the hoses should be protected from mechanical damage and the operator should be protected against the risk of hose burst by guards or protective sheaths around the hoses.

128   The noise and vibration levels inside the compartment should be kept as low as is reasonably practicable, allowing the operator to hear warnings and alarms at all times, including all public address announcements. If this is not practicable, alternative methods should be provided, eg by radio communication or visual displays. Hearing protection incorporating communications is acceptable provided it does not cause discomfort to the operator, especially over long shift periods.

129   You should provide a method of two-way communication between the crane operator and people involved with lifting operations on the installation, the master of the supply vessel and the central control/radio room on the installation. Hands-free operation of the communication system is preferred.

130   A fire extinguisher, life jacket and smoke hood should be conveniently fitted inside the compartment or local to the control stand (along with other life saving equipment that may be required). This requirement may be waived for remote control compartments located on the installation itself.

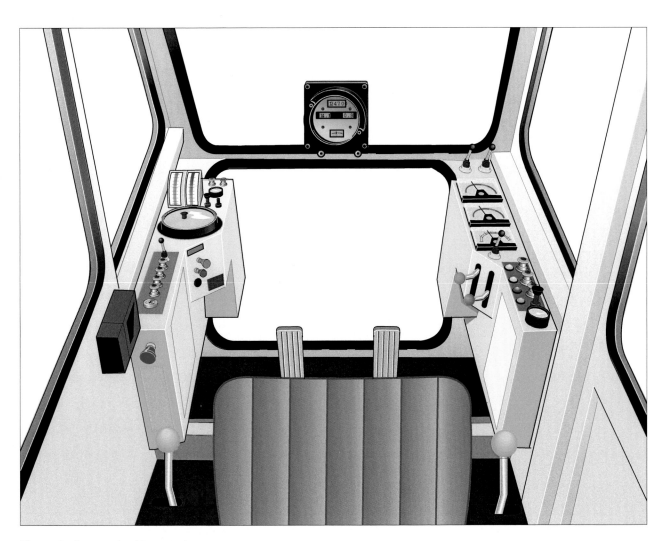

Figure 3 Crane cab with controls

Controls

131 The effort required to operate the controls should comply with a recognised code or standard. On release, controls should return to the neutral position, automatically activating the appropriate braking systems. Control systems using electronic logic should be designed so that failure or malfunction of the system will default to a safe situation irrespective of the operational status or configuration of the crane at the time.

132 An emergency stop device, inhibiting further use of the prime mover, should be provided in the operator's compartment or stand and at the entrance to the prime mover location (machinery house). It should be available for ready use but designed and located to prevent inadvertent operation. Alarms should be provided to alert the crane operator to any power loss or hydraulic system failure. Other alarms or instrumentation should be suitably labelled and should be clearly visible during all hours of crane operation, including hours of darkness.

133 All crane controls should be clearly marked to show their function and mode of operation and should be visible at all times, including the hours of darkness. The controls should be arranged to prevent unintentional operation of the crane or loss of control of the load. As far as possible, controls should follow ergonomic principles so that there is a logical connection between the directional movement of the control lever and the motion of the crane. For example:

- for raising the load and for raising the boom, movement of the control lever should be towards the operator;
- for lowering the load or lowering the hook, movement of the control lever should be away from the operator;
- for slewing left, or right, the movement of the control lever should be to the left or right;
- when changing the length of telescopic booms, movement of the control lever should be away from the operator to extend the boom and towards the operator to retract it.

Hooks and hook blocks

Design and manufacture

134 The design, manufacture and marking of hooks, including hooks which are part of the pennant line, should be in accordance with relevant national, European or international standards.

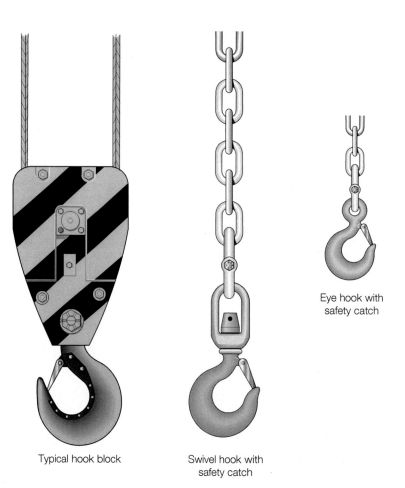

Typical hook block

Swivel hook with safety catch

Eye hook with safety catch

Figure 4 Some types of hooks found on cranes and lifting equipment

135   The hook or any other first-order lifting device should be designed to prevent any snagging.

136   A hook block that has a threaded shank retained by means of a nut should be designed to prevent moisture and dirt from entering the space between the threaded shank and the bearing nut. Hooks which may be used for sub-sea operations should have suitable protection for all bearings and threaded components. Effective locking arrangements should be provided to hold the nut captive in service.

137   The safe working load (SWL) should be legibly marked on every hook, identifiable with an in-date test document. The method of marking should not affect the strength of the hook.

138   Every hook block should carry a non-removable plate showing the following information:

■   the safe working load in tonnes and decimals of a tonne to one decimal point except for the numbers 0.25 and 0.75;
■   an identification mark to relate the block to its document of test and examination;
■   the diameter of the wire rope for which it is designed; and
■   identification of any component of the block which is manufactured from special steels or alloys.

See also *Marking* in paragraphs 78-82.

Operation

139   Hooks should be fitted with an effective safety latch or mechanism that ensures slings or pennant wire are positively held captive under all operating circumstances. Unauthorised removal of the slings or pennant wire, whether loaded or unloaded, should not be permitted. The safety latch or mechanism should not be secured to the hook by welding, unless approved by the manufacturer or competent person.

Testing

140   Hook blocks should be dismantled, inspected and subjected to non-destructive testing examination at intervals not exceeding five years. Blocks fitted with new or modified parts (in the primary load path) should be overload (proof load) tested appropriate to their SWL. Procedures for strip-down, refurbishment and test should be approved by the competent person. See also paragraphs 47-51.

141   Dismantling and examination after load testing should be at the discretion of the competent person. However, as a guide, this would generally only be required where:

■   the block is of new or prototype design with no proven service record;
■   the block has been (or is suspected to have been) subjected to an excessive overload, where damage or deformation of components may have occurred; or
■   a site modification has been carried out or new materials or components have been installed.

142   Testing of the blocks after reassembly may be waived by a competent person provided that:

■   reassembly was carried out in accordance with the approved drawings and procedures and to a statement of conformity approved by a competent person; and/or
■   the competent person is assured that the assembly is correct after visual appraisal of the assembled hook block.

Maintenance, repair and modification

143   Repairing hooks by welding or heat treatment is bad practice and should not be permitted.

144   The maximum permitted wear on hooks should not normally exceed 5% of the 'as new' dimensions. However, with the agreement of the competent person, localised wear between 5% and 10% may be allowable in any one area of the hook.

Slewbearings and slewbearing fasteners

Design and manufacture

145   For cranes which operate in a permanently fixed or permanently tied-down mode, slewbearings for offshore use should meet design and manufacturing standards approved by a competent person.

146   Slewbearing fasteners should be designed, manufactured and tested to agreed recognised codes and standards eg BS 3692 - Grade 10.9.[14] Any approved equivalent fasteners should be specified with rolled threads after heat treatment. Fasteners should facilitate through-type fixing over an effective length of at least five diameters. Fasteners should be equally spaced on a constant pitch circle - unequal spacing (part sector bolting) should be avoided.

Selecting suitable equipment

147   For cranes operating in free-standing mode, with lifting duties based on the stability of the crane, the crane manufacturer's standard slewbearing may be considered suitable. This is provided it can be shown that it is not limited by strength and has adequate fatigue resistance, raceway wear sufficiency and notch toughness for the prescribed operational temperatures and service duties.

Inspection

148   Slewbearings used offshore should either be subject to removal, strip-down and examination at intervals, or be subjected to a system of in-situ monitoring, both agreed by a competent person. The period between examinations depends on the bearing type and construction and the degree of monitoring which is carried out (see Table 2). You should agree with the competent person all procedures for examining and monitoring the condition of the internals of the slewbearing. As a minimum, the procedures should include grease sampling techniques for laboratory analysis,

and 'rocking' tests to check for undue play in the bearing. When carrying out 'rocking' tests, the whole crane should be effectively secured.

149 Where a crane is fitted with retainers or other devices which would stop it becoming detached from its pedestal if the slewbearing failed, the competent person may agree to extend the examination intervals of the slewbearing.

150 Examinations should be carried out using equipment that has been approved by both the slewbearing manufacturer and a competent person, who should have the necessary qualifications and experience in this type of examination and also be conversant with the equipment used for the examination.

151 Before any examination, the competent person should be given the necessary documentation to make an accurate assessment of the slewbearing. The documentation should include the slewbearing manufacturer's calculations, which should indicate the design loads, the allowable stresses for the slewbearing elements and slewbearing fasteners, safety factors and material specifications. Engineering drawings may also be required, to facilitate dimensional checks of the slewbearing components.

152 As a minimum, the examination should include:

■ an examination of the raceway surfaces;

■ a subsurface examination to identify any significant defects. This should be carried out in areas where defects could have a detrimental effect on the integrity of the slewbearing. Acceptance of any subsurface defects should be agreed with the competent person.

■ where the raceways are hardened, an examination of the raceway through the full depth into the core material for significant defects. Any defects should be rectified and the hardness depth rechecked; this check should also be carried out after any rework has been done to the hardened surfaces.

■ an examination of all safety-critical sections, ie highly loaded corner radii etc. A safety-critical section is one where failure could cause a catastrophic failure of the slewbearing and subsequent loss of the crane. You should give particular attention to safety-critical sections where there is the possibility of neighbourhood reaction or crack propagation.

■ the condition of the rolling elements, cages and seals; and

■ the retaining device on designs where this device is an integral part of the slewbearing.

153 Any rework should be carried out only after agreement you have reached with the refurbisher and a competent person. The refurbisher should satisfy the competent person that any rework will not compromise or degrade the

Table 2 Examination periods for slewbearings

Slewbearings incorporating internal rolling elements should be subject to periodic examination as agreed with the competent person. The following table gives general guidance regarding the nature of the examination. If a risk assessment approach is to be used in place of defined examination periods, this philosophy and methodology must be agreed with the competent person.

Category 1 designation	Slewbearings that do not comply with the requirements of paragraphs 145-153 of this guidance.	Slewbearings to be removed from the crane at intervals not exceeding three years, stripped down and subjected to a thorough examination by a suitably qualified person(s). The designated competent person should be present during this examination.
Category 2 designation	Slewbearings which comply with the requirements of paragraphs 145-153 of this guidance.	Periods for slewbearing removal, strip-down and examination to be agreed with the competent person. Inspection and examination should be carried out by a suitably qualified person(s). The designated competent person should be present during the examination.
Category 3 designation	Slewbearings which comply with the requirements of paragraphs 145-153 and paragraphs 154-162 of this guidance.	Subject to agreement with the competent person, slewbearing removal from the crane, strip-down and inspection is not required provided that results from the monitoring systems show no significant defects in the slewbearing internals and/or components. These results must have been approved by the competent person and an approval certificate obtained. See note below.

Note: The approval certificate should be kept current by resubmission on an annual basis to the competent person/verification body. All data submitted to the competent person/verification body in order to obtain deferrals for continued operation of the slewbearing should be readily retrievable for inspection by the Regulatory Authority when required.

strength or capacity of the slewbearing. After reassembly of the slewbearing, the competent person should issue a signed approval certificate. The slewbearing should not be refitted to the crane until a reassembly approval certificate has been obtained from the competent person. If, in the opinion of the competent person, any rework which would be carried out on the slewbearing that could compromise the original strength or capacity of the slewbearing, then the slewbearing shall not be refurbished or put back into service.

Monitoring requirements for Category 3 slewbearings and fasteners

154   The monitoring requirements of triple roller, cross roller and shear ball slewbearings are given in paragraphs 155-159.

155   **Condition monitoring systems,** or facilities to enable condition monitoring to be carried out, will be required for:

(a)   triple roller bearing type slewing rings; and
(b)   cross roller and shear ball-type slewing rings, unless a risk assessment is undertaken which shows that no possible configuration can occur where this design of slewbearing can fail in a catastrophic manner during service.

156   Condition monitoring systems should be capable of detecting defects in all safety-critical radii and where neighbourhood reactions and crack propagation could lead to the catastrophic failure of the bearing in service. They should be of proven reliability and be acceptable to the competent person. Scanning and data retrieval intervals should be agreed with and kept for inspection by the competent person/verification body.

157   **Grease sampling analysis:** Grease samples should be extracted from the slewbearing at dedicated points using methods acceptable to the competent person. They should be analysed using procedures and techniques agreed by the competent person. Intervals of sample retrieval, analysis procedure and the logging of results should be acceptable to the competent person. You should retain the results for inspection on demand.

158   **Rocking motion tests** should be carried out by a qualified person experienced with the methodology and use of any equipment required. A log should be kept showing the rocking motion trends and the allowable rocking motion limit for each type of slewbearing installed. You should keep the results of rocking tests for inspection by the competent person.

159   **Loading history of crane:** You should keep loading records and an authenticated loading history of the crane for examination by the competent person. Loading history should be recorded through a data recorder linked to the crane's safe load indicator system. Data logging equipment, techniques for retrieval, retrieval intervals and logging procedures should be agreed by the competent person.

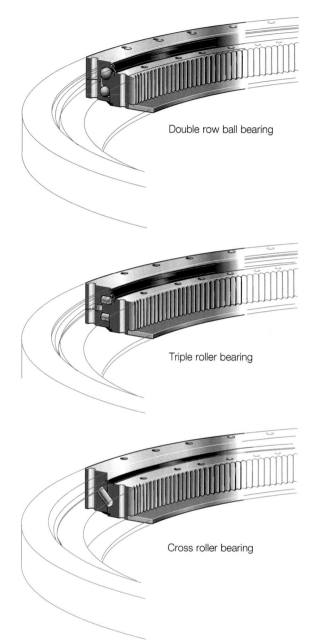

Double row ball bearing

Triple roller bearing

Cross roller bearing

Figure 5 Types of slew bearings

160   **Fastener examination:** Bolt installation examination, inspection intervals and replacement criteria should be according to agreed procedures. You should keep a log of bolt inspections and replacements for ready inspection by a competent person.

161   Monitoring requirements and examination periods for slewbearings may be amended by the competent person, depending on the type of slewbearing, fastening arrangements and retention devices incorporated. Paragraphs 155-159 give general, indicative monitoring and inspection requirements for triple roller, cross roller and shear ball slewbearings which should be acceptable to the competent person.

162 If a recognised integral catcher is built into the design of the slewbearing, the competent person has the discretion to amend some of the requirements in paragraphs 155-160. You must discuss, agree and document any amendments.

Operation

163 When refurbished slewbearings need to be stored for extended periods, the storage instructions of the manufacturer should be observed.

164 You should agree the procedures for installation and tightening of slewbearing fasteners with the competent person. Fasteners should be tightened according to the recommendations provided by the slewbearing manufacturer. The pre-tension should be recorded at installation and at periodical inspections. The use of fasteners with a load monitoring facility, either as an integral part of the fastener or via load washers, is recommended. You should agree a planned maintenance schedule with the competent person for the inspection of fasteners and to check their in-service tightness.

Hydraulic systems

Selecting suitable equipment

165 Components used in hydraulic systems should be suitable for continued and effective operation in offshore service conditions. They should be selected by the supplier to withstand dynamic effects arising from the crane's operation, overload testing and the corrosive nature of the environment and of any additional local contaminants. Certain types of oils may encourage biological growth, and steps should be taken to prevent any damage this may present to the equipment.

Operation

166 Where hydraulic powered systems are used to drive the crane's main services, the driving fluid and its containment and distribution system is considered to be a primary load path system. The crane operator should be informed of the main circuit hydraulic pressure, any boost/make-up system pressure and any significant loss of fluid. Failure of any component resulting in loss of fluid or pressure should not cause the crane to operate in an uncontrolled manner.

167 The build-up of corrosive oxides may cause seizure of valves or damage to piping and fittings. All components (particularly valves) which are critical to the safe control and operation of the crane should be protected against this build-up.

168 Where hydraulic ram-type actuators are used:

- the ram rods should be adequately protected against corrosion;
- in the event of loss of hydraulic power, the rams should be prevented from any extension or retraction, ie they should hold indefinitely without creep; and

- the hydraulic system should provide effective control for lowering the boom or load safely in the event of any power loss.

Maintenance, repair and modification

169 Hydraulic fluids should be regularly checked for correct quantity and consistency. Oil sampling and analysis methods should be to procedures agreed with a competent person. You should ensure that the hydraulic fluid is kept to acceptable cleanliness levels, for example by regular sampling and testing in accordance with ISO 4406,[15] to assess its condition and suitability for further service. You should provide a filtered pump-fill system situated on the reservoir. The reservoir should incorporate a breather system that prevents ingress of moisture and the saline environment, eg by using bladder-type breathing systems or pressurised reservoirs. It should also incorporate high and low fluid level indicators. The crane operator should be informed of fluid levels below the low level mark.

170 Lubricating oils used in safety-critical equipment such as winch gearboxes or slewing gearboxes should be sampled using an effective qualitative analysis system to check that the debris/particle content remains within acceptable limits for continued safe use of the crane.

171 Hydraulic relief valve settings should be maintained in accordance with the manufacturer's requirements and should not be tampered with. Where relief valve settings need to be reset or adjusted, this should be carried out by someone competent in these operations.

Prime movers

Diesel engine prime movers

172 For cranes which are powered by a diesel engine prime mover, you should ensure the following:

- All exposed rotating parts such as fans, flywheels and couplings should be suitably guarded to prevent injury.
- The hot surfaces of exhaust systems, turbo chargers and the engine itself should be suitably guarded or routed to prevent operators being burned.
- Diesel exhaust systems should be routed so that exhaust emissions cannot enter machinery compartments or the crane operator's compartment or stand.
- Diesel fuel tanks should not be located above the level of the fuel injectors. There should be an effective system for collecting any spillage of fuel in the filling area for immediate disposal on the installation. If the fuel tank is in the same compartment as the engine, a remotely operated shut-down valve should be fitted as near to the tank as possible.
- Diesel-powered cranes which can be used for man-riding purposes should have a secondary independent means of starting via a readily available

power source other than that used for the primary starting system. For pneumatic starting systems this requirement could be met by having rig air available from the installation, which could be quickly connected to the main engine starting system. Where it is not possible to incorporate a secondary start system there should be a way of enabling the personnel carrier and its occupants to be readily returned to a safe area.

- Diesel engines should be fitted with the following:
  - a mechanically operated device which will provide local shut-down of the engine;
  - a device that prevents backdriving or overhauling of the diesel engine, unless this is incorporated in the transmission system of the crane; and
  - fire/smoke alarms which are clearly audible at the operator's compartment or control station and can be heard under all operational noise levels.
- Diesel engines which may be required to operate in potentially explosive atmospheres should comply with the recommendations in paragraphs 74-77.

Electric prime movers

173   For cranes which are powered by an electric motor prime mover, you should ensure the following:

- All exposed rotating parts such as couplings or fans should be suitably guarded to prevent injury.
- Electric motors should be suitably earthed using straps protected against the effects of condensation and corrosion.
- Electric motor prime movers should incorporate the following:
  - a warning located at the operator's compartment or station of any overheating of the motor windings;
  - a warning located at the operator's compartment or station of failure of power supply to the motor;
  - protection against overspeeding; and
  - fire/smoke alarms which are clearly audible at the operator's compartment or station under all operational noise levels.

174   Electric motor prime movers which may need to operate in potentially explosive atmospheres should comply with the recommendations in paragraphs 74-77.

Emergency electrical supplies

175   Where appropriate, you should provide emergency electrical supplies (where battery backup is not already available) for the following crane systems and functions:

- helicopter warning lights;
- lighting of emergency escape routes;
- the crane control system;
- safe load indicator and any associated data recording system; and
- diesel engine controls, where this is practicable.

176   For cranes which are electrically powered and are designated suitable for man-riding purposes, you should provide a secondary electrical supply to operate the personnel carrier system in the event of primary supply power failure. Where this is not possible there should be a way to return the personnel carrier and its occupants readily to a safe area if there is a power supply failure.

Safety systems

177   All variable geometry cranes used on offshore installations, particularly those used for dynamic lifting operations from attendant vessels, should be suitably safeguarded against:

- dynamic/shock loads;
- overloads (in-plane and lateral to the boom); and
- overhauling of the load hoist (by the load and/or other forces), boom hoist, slew and travel drive systems.

178   Some of the safety systems in Table 3 are specific requirements of the LOLER ACOP,[7] others are recommendations of this guidance. Table 3 shows a summary of the systems.

Gross overload/overmoment protection (GOP)

179   Wherever possible, cranes involved with lifting activities in various sea states should be protected against overloads and overmoments caused by the crane hook or load becoming snagged on the attendant vessel structure and/or its deck cargo. This applies whether they are permanently fixed, tied-down or in free-standing mode. This protection should not be activated by the transient loading conditions that normally occur during lifting operations and should not cut out or stall the prime mover.

180   The GOP should be set to activate at a safe margin above the crane's maximum permissible lifting capacity for any given radius, and at a safe margin below any loading conditions that may cause the failure of a structural or mechanical component. Procedures for periodically testing the GOP (controlled activation) should be agreed with the crane supplier and competent person and provided in the crane's operating manual. The GOP should not be influenced by any controlled overload testing undertaken on the crane. Healthy (fully functional) status of the GOP should be indicated - preferably in the operator's compartment or at the control stand.

181   As part of the GOP system, you should consider fitting a low fracture tailing rope to allow the main load hoist rope to pay out and clear the hook in a controlled manner, if the supply vessel sails away from the installation with the hook or load still attached. See also paragraph 118.

182   Where it is not practicable to fit a GOP system, eg on older model cranes, alternative measures should be approved by a competent person.

Table 3 Summary of principal recommended safety systems in paragraphs 179-200

Code designation A is a requirement of LOLER ACOP[7]
Code designation B is recommended by this guidance

System		Code	Comment	Cranes used for deck lifts only
	All types			
#1	GOP	B	Used for boat lifts	N/A
2	Safe load indicator (SLI)	A	All lifts	yes
3	Data recorder	B	For slewing bearing deferrals	Optional
#4	Auto tension	B	Used for boat lifts	N/A
#5	Slew torque limiters	B	Used for boat lifts	If required
#6	Emergency load release	B	Used for boat lifts	N/A
7	Overhoist limits	A		yes
8	Overlower limits	A		yes
9	Overspeed control	B		yes
10	Min/max radius limits	A		yes*
11	Slewing limits	A		yes
12	Crane travel	A	Where applicable	Mobiles only**

* Minimum radius may be achieved by fully stroking the luff rams to their physical limits. At maximum radius, there should be approximately 75 mm of free stroke remaining in the rams, ie the rams should not 'bottom out' when operating at maximum radius.

** Includes cranes which travel on rail systems mounted at deck level or where the hookload/load is traversed close to deck level.

\# Where it is not practicable to fit these systems (on some existing cranes) a risk assessment should be carried out by a competent person. This should indicate the measures taken to mitigate the hazards from operating the crane without these systems in place.

Rated Capacity Indicator

183   The crane should be fitted with a Rated Capacity Indicator (RCI) giving details of the actual/permissible loads (at the appropriate radius) and moments over the working area where the load is lifted or set down. Selecting the safe working load and number of falls of rope at the hook block depends on the operating radius and prevailing sea state. This information should be readily available to the operator.

184   For telescopic boom cranes, the RCI should be capable of automatically resetting the appropriate duty ratings applicable to any change of the boom length.

185   You should consider implementing a system (for example a data recorder) which will provide a continuous recording of static and dynamic loads, moments and other operational parameters to give a full history of the crane's operations. This data may be used to assess maintenance or service requirements or the timing of removing the slewbearing for thorough examination. If you install as part of the RCI a data recorder which needs to be operated in a potentially explosive atmosphere, the system must be suitably protected.

186   The RCI should give the crane operator a clear and continuous visual warning when the hook load exceeds a figure of between 90% and 97.5% of the safe working load of the crane for a given radius. The system should automatically give a continuous audible warning to the operator and to anyone else in the area when the hook load is between 102.5% and 110% of the safe working load of the crane for any given radius. The RCI should have facilities for:

■   manually checking the healthy status of the indicator and data recorder;
■   checking the percentage accuracy of the indicator over the full duty spectrum; and
■   carrying out overload testing of the crane; and
■   it should not be possible for the crane operator to incorrectly input into the RCI the number of falls of rope that are actually configured on the main/whip hoist, any incorrect input should initiate a warning signal on the RCI panel.

187   An audible and visual warning should be incorporated, responding to any overmoments that may arise beyond those permitted for the crane's operational service conditions.

188   The British Standard for automatic safe load indicators is BS 7262.[16] The European Standard for automatic rated capacity indicators is EN 12077-2.[17]

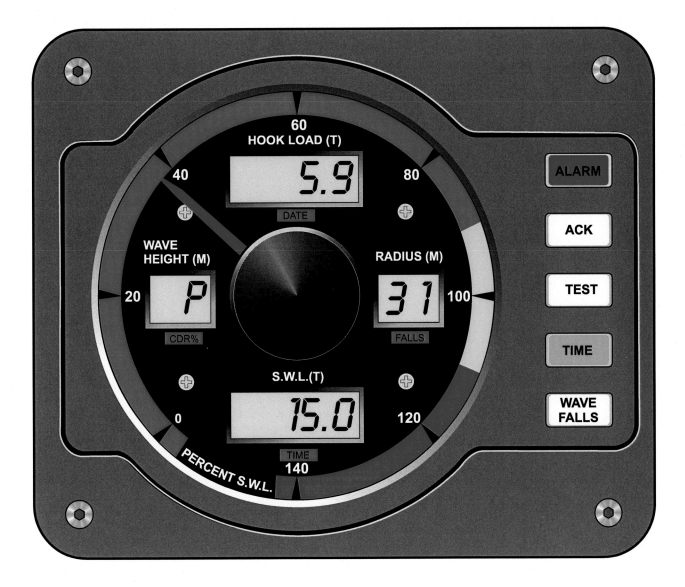

Figure 6 Typical rated capacity indicator

Wave following/constant tension systems

189 You should consider providing a wave following/constant tension system that keeps the crane hook/load in synchronous speed with the rise and fall of the supply vessel. This kind of system prevents any slack in the crane hoist rope or slings as the motion of the vessel is followed. The tension in the hoist rope and slings should never exceed that which would otherwise be generated by the suspended load. This system should be designed so that it can only be selected in a deliberate act by the crane operator. It should not be possible to activate the system under any other situation during normal operations of the crane, ie with any load on the hook. The system should be failsafe so that any fault in the constant tension system when it is operational immediately and safely returns the crane to its normal functional operating mode.

190 The rise and fall of the hook load in this mode should be indicated in the control console, allowing the operator to judge when best to lift the load from the supply vessel with minimal shock loading to the crane, eg on a rising wave or at the crest of a wave. The decision whether to activate the constant tension mode should normally be left to the crane operator.

Slew torque limiters

191 A competent person should assess the risk of excessive sideloads being applied to the boom. If these loads would be large enough to cause structural or mechanical damage, you should consider providing a limiting slew torque capability to prevent undue sideloads happening under any circumstances.

Emergency load release

192 You should provide an effective means for the operator to activate immediate release of the load. The release device should be in the crane operator's compartment or control stand. It should be designed and located to prevent

accidental operation and it should be activated only by a 'deliberate act' by the operator. The design and location should be different from that of the emergency stop device referred to in paragraph 132. The device, when operated, should stay put, allowing uninterrupted load release. Once operated, it should not be possible to regain control of a load already in load release mode. Under these conditions, the rope should spool from the winch drum in a controlled manner, ie the rope should not bunch, loop or otherwise cause snagging.

Overhoist limit

193   You should provide an overhoist limiting device that prevents the hook block(s) from being raised into contact with the boom head. The device should stop any motion of the crane that might cause this, including raising the hook via the load hoist system, booming up or down or extending the boom. The device should give prior warning to the crane operator of any impending cut-out of the system which prevents any further hoisting of the hook. It should be possible to effect controlled drive-down of the hook after activating the device. The device should remain effective in the event of extreme out-of-verticality of the load line.

Overlower limit

194   You should provide means to ensure that lowering the hook/load cannot extend beyond the three residual turns of rope which should remain on the drum in any configuration of the crane. This is unless the crane operator is deliberately directed to lower the hook/load, for example by activating the GOP system or by operating the emergency load release.

Overspeed control

195   You should provide means to prevent the load from descending or the boom from overspeeding under all loading configurations. This is likely to apply mainly to cranes with mechanical transmission systems, as on hydraulic transmission system cranes this is done automatically. It may not be practicable on older cranes which utilise mechanical transmission systems to incorporate a device which complies with this requirement. In this case, you should consider possible alternatives such as providing the operator with an indication of the winch drum or line speed, up to the maximum specified speed. An acceptable method would be a variable audible tone that is activated when the maximum drum speed is approached and which remains at constant pitch when it is reached. A competent person should verify the integrity of any system(s) fitted.

Maximum and minimum radius limits

196   To prevent the crane from exceeding its operating range, you should fit boom angle limiting devices. These should provide the crane operator with visual alarms before activating automatic cut-outs that prevent any further movement of the boom beyond its specified working range. Re-establishing boom hoist control or the use of any override systems should require a deliberate act by the

crane operator. It is acceptable to override in some circumstances, for example when lowering the boom head to deck level or into its rest stand. Boom backstops, preferably of the shock absorbing type, should be provided to prevent the boom from travelling rearward of its minimum radius limit (this may be caused by gusting winds or the movement of a floating installation). Where booms are raised and lowered by hydraulic rams, these should incorporate suitable end-of-stroke cushioning.

197   Boom rams should have a margin of residual stroke when lifting loads at maximum radius.

Slewing limits

198   Where cranes operate close to other structures on the installation, they should be fitted with a visual and audible alarm located in the operator's compartment or control stand. This should warn the operator if the crane boom approaches these structures as the crane is slewed. The slewing limit device should be linked to the boom hoist system to allow for changes in boom angle which may change the proximity of any approaching hazard when the crane is slewed.

199   It may not be practicable to fit slewing limit alarms, for example on mobile cranes where the action of travelling may be difficult to accommodate. In this case, the competent person should ensure that procedures are in place to prevent the boom, or any part of the crane, from coming into contact with other structures.

Crane travelling warning

200   Mobile cranes should be provided with both audible and visual (flashing) warnings which operate when the crane is travelling.

201   A banksman should also be in attendance when the crane is travelling.

Principal recommendations

202   A summary of principal recommendations for variable geometry slewing cranes is given in Table 4.

Table 4 Summary of principal recommendations for variable geometry slewing cranes as appropriate to type and operational use

Principal features	Essential	Desirable	See note
CRANE DUTIES			
To agreed relevant codes	YES		3
Limited by component strength - crane tied down	YES		1
Limited by sea state	YES		
Limited by offlead angle	YES		
Limited by sidelead angle	YES		
Limited by wind speed	YES		
Limited by dynamic enhanced loading conditions	YES		
Limited by heel/trim/pitch - floating installations	YES		
Limited by relative movements - installation/support vessel	YES		
DECK LOADING			
Max loads generated by lifting operations	YES		1
Max loads generated by travelling - with/without hook load	YES		1
PERFORMANCE			
Hoist speed - sufficient to prevent re-impact	YES		
Speed of boom hoist and slew - to ensure vertical lift	YES		
Prevention of uncontrolled motions - load and boom hoists	YES		
Prevention of uncontrolled slewing	YES		
Prime mover stall prevention - power management system	YES		5
BRAKING SYSTEMS			
All service brakes to be spring set to fail-safe	YES		
At least one dynamically rated brake to be situated as near as possible to the load/boom hoist drum	YES		
Secondary braking by hydraulic system etc		YES	
Boom hoist pawl		YES	2
Brakes to be protected against environmental and other sources of contamination		YES	
DRUMS AND SHEAVES			
Controlled rope spooling	YES		
Captive rope system under slack wire conditions	YES		
Rotation of drum - direct sight or indication to operator		YES	
Level wind condition - diving winches only	YES		
ROPES/TERMINATIONS			
Low rotational type for main/whip hoists		YES	
Direct access to rope anchorage/terminations		YES	
Ropes and terminations to recognised standards	YES		
OPERATOR'S COMPARTMENT			
Cabin located on slewing structure		YES	
Clear line of sight from boom tip to supply vessel deck	YES		
Window washers/wipers/demisters	YES		
Internal temperature controls/noise levels		YES	
Safety glass windows	YES		
Rear viewing window for travelling cranes	YES		1

Principal features	Essential	Desirable	See note
CONTROLS			
Hand controller centre to neutral on release	YES		
Hand controller movements directional and proportional with crane motions	YES		
Layout/operations to recognised ergonomic principles	YES		
No excessive vibration levels at control station		YES	
MATERIALS AND WELDED STRUCTURES			
Chemical properties to agreed recognised standards			3
Mechanical properties to agreed recognised standards			3
Heat treatment procedures/EC certificate of conformity			
Welding to agreed recognised standard			
Welding to be continuous			7
SAFETY SYSTEMS			
Gross overload protection - GOP	YES		
Safe load indicator - SLI	YES		
Data recording facilities		YES	
Constant/auto tension system		YES	
Prime mover stall and overspeed prevention system	YES		
Emergency load release - anti-snag system	YES		
Emergency stop	YES		
Overhoist/overlower warning/cut-out	YES		
Max/min radius warning/cut-out	YES		
Boom back stops	YES		2
PA/radio communications	YES		
Fire and gas systems	YES		
Audible and visual warning when crane is travelling	YES		1
Aircraft warning light	YES		2
Load/boom lower speed indicator - mechanical transmission only		YES	
OPERATIONS IN EXPLOSIVE ATMOSPHERES			
Flameproof diesel to recognised standard	YES		
Electrical systems to recognised standard, eg ATEX	YES		
Electric motors to recognised standard	YES		
SLEWBEARINGS AND SLEWBEARING FASTENERS			
Slewbearing designed to agreed offshore standards	YES		
Slewbearing designed to agreed standards - mobile cranes		YES	1
Retainer/retaining ring		YES	
Grease sampling facility	YES		
Rocking test check		YES	
Built-in condition monitoring facility		YES	
Inspection and monitoring procedures	YES		
Bolt properties to agreed standards	YES		
Through bolt-type fixing		YES	
Rolled threads after heat treatment	YES		
In-situ load monitoring facility		YES	6
Agreed tightening and monitoring procedures	YES		

Principal features	Essential	Desirable	See note
ACCESS AND ESCAPE			
Built-in - to facilitate routine checks and maintenance etc		YES	
Emergency escape - regardless of crane configuration	YES		
CORROSION PROTECTION			
Seizure prevention of critical components	YES		
Corrosion prevention of critical fasteners - slewbearing	YES		
Corrosion protection of principle fasteners		YES	
HOOK BLOCK ASSEMBLIES			
Designed to recognised standards	YES		
Inspection and testing by agreement	YES		3
Positive captive holding of slings	YES		
OTHER ITEMS			
Inspection frequencies	YES		
Mothballing - with potential start-up	YES		
Operating procedures, limitations etc	YES		
Inspection/maintenance/service	YES		6
Man-riding operations	YES		

[1] Applicable to mobile cranes only.

[2] Not applicable to ram luff-type cranes.

[3] The terms 'agreed' and 'agreement' are taken to mean those between you or the competent person and the crane manufacturer or supplier.

[4] These recommendations are considered to be practical and in keeping with established good practices. The listings are not exhaustive and variations are expected to arise according to the crane type, operational service and location. You should agree any technical, operational and any other variances with the crane manufacturer.

[5] Diesel engine prime movers only.

[6] Inspection, maintenance and pre-start procedures should be compatible with the use of the crane, eg frequent or infrequent use, crane left idle for long periods, mothballing.

[7] Continuous welds may be required on certain structural parts of the crane to protect the internals from corrosion.

Cranes - overhead/gantry travelling types and wire rope hoists

Overhead and gantry cranes

Selecting suitable equipment

203   You should provide a mechanical anti-derailment device that holds the crane captive to its rails at all times, including during sea transit. The anti-derailment device should apply to both long- and cross-travel systems.

204   You should fit over-travel limits or cut-outs, supplemented by energy-absorbing end-of-travel stops, for both long- and cross-travel systems.

205   You should provide all powered travelling systems with effective brakes which prevent any further movement of the crane or load when the hand or pendant controller is released. For manually-operated travelling systems, brakes are only required where there are significant movements of

the floating installation. You should consider using rack and pinion drive systems for both long- and cross-travel functions, under arduous lifting or environmental conditions or where there may be movements of the installation.

Operation

206   Where more than one crane is used on one rail system, each should be fitted with collision warning and prevention systems supplemented with energy absorbing buffers.

207   For storm and sea transit of floating installations, cranes should be effectively tied back to the installation.

208   Rail systems which the whole crane is fixed to should be secured, inspected, checked for being flat and parallel, and maintained in accordance with the crane supplier's recommendations. Rails which are located at deck level should be suitably guarded against possible trip hazards.

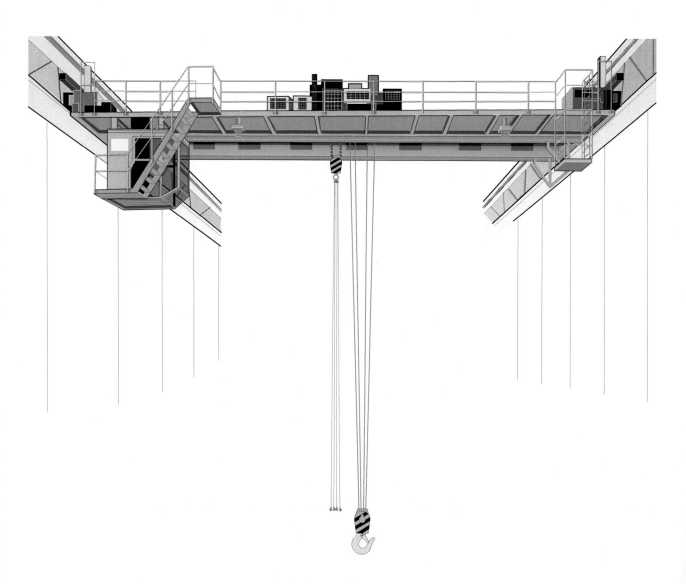

Figure 7 Overhead crane

209 You should provide safe access and escape routes on cranes which are fitted with an operator's cabin or platform, walkways, ladders, stairs and handholds. There should be a safe means of escape regardless of the crane's location along the rails. Cranes which are operated from deck level, for example by pendant or manual methods, should be provided with dedicated unobstructed walkways. The travelling speed of these cranes should not be greater than the walking pace of the operator. You should also provide safe means of access for inspections and maintenance.

210 Cranes which operate on rails located at deck level should be provided with audible and visual warnings which alert everyone in the area when the crane is travelling.

Cranes and hoists (wire rope type)

Design and manufacture

211 The SWL of all crane and hoist units should be clearly marked on each side of the crane bridge and on hoists at a suitable point. This should be legible to people at deck level.

Selecting suitable equipment

212 All hoist brakes should be spring set, failsafe type. The hoist brakes and drive system should be enclosed and not exposed to contaminants. In the event of power failure, it must be possible to operate the brake manually to lower the suspended load safely.

213 The hoist system should be provided with limits or cut-outs that prevent overhoisting and overlowering of the hook. These limits and cut-outs are safety critical. You should consider providing dual limits/cut-out systems, especially on the overhoist function.

214 Where the weight of the load is unknown, or where two cranes or hoists are used to lift a load in tandem, a load limiting or load indicating device should be provided. (Note: This requirement only covers loads greater than 1000 kg or, where applicable, when the overturning moment is greater than 40 000 Nm.)

215 For powered cranes and hoists, you should provide an emergency stop at the control station. Activating the emergency stop should arrest all motions of the crane and hoist as well as shutting down the crane/hoist power supply.

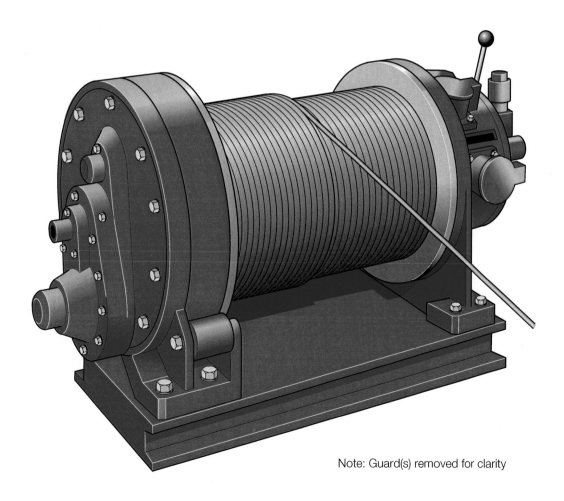

Note: Guard(s) removed for clarity

Figure 8 General purpose winch

216   Where gantry cranes and hoists are operated by a pendant controller:

■   buttons should be protected by a raised annular guard;
■   all button and lever or joystick controllers should be protected against inadvertent activation;
■   the degree of protection should be compatible with environmental conditions;
■   controllers should be 'fail-safe'; and
■   effective isolation of the power supply should be provided.

217   For equipment operating in potentially explosive atmospheres, see paragraphs 74-77.

Testing

218   Powered cranes and hoists should be subjected to an overload test agreed by a competent person. This should include all elements of the winch, and long-travel and cross-travel drive systems. Details of the test should be documented and validated by a competent person.

Other lifting equipment

Chain hoists and chain lever hoists

Design and manufacture

219   Chain hoists, both powered and manual, should be designed to recognised national, European or international standards.

220   Manual chain/lever hoists are usually manufactured only to basic commercial standards. When selecting a chain/lever hoist for use offshore, the competent person should ensure that it is suitable for the purpose and the environmental conditions. Manufacturers and suppliers of chain/lever hoists should ensure that operating instructions and thorough examination and maintenance procedures are specific to the type of equipment and to the conditions prevailing at the point of use. The instructions and procedures should identify all sensitivities and limiting factors that may apply with the use of chain/lever hoists offshore. Ingress of water, particularly saltwater, drilling powders/muds, silt and the saline marine environment itself can greatly diminish the effectiveness of braking systems and the overall condition (which could be affected by corrosion) of manual chain/lever hoists. For chain and lever hoists which are used sub-sea, special requirements are needed. Guidance on this subject is given in the Lifting Equipment Engineers Association handbook, publication reference LEEA 033.[18]

221   Manufacturers and suppliers should ensure that lubricants for the moving elements are suitable for the conditions. Users should follow appropriate practice for this type of equipment. The supplier should provide details to ensure the correct storage of chain/lever hoists in a marine environment.

Figure 9 Chain hoist

222   The SWL should be clearly and permanently marked on the hoist.

223   Where chain hoists are used in an explosive atmosphere, they should be suitably designed, constructed and maintained for this purpose. Equipment that is suitable for use in potentially explosive atmospheres should be marked accordingly and be supported with the appropriate documentation of conformity. For equipment manufactured and installed before 1997, the minimum requirement will be the zone classification where it can be used. See also paragraphs 74-77.

Selecting suitable equipment

224   The chain hoist should be selected by a competent person who should take due account of its intended operational duties, including factors such as:

■   frequency of use;
■   service life;
■   conditions of use; and
■   state of loading.

Where chain hoists are to be used for general purpose lifting operations and these factors may be difficult to assess accurately, the competent person should select the most suitable capacity hoist, making conservative assumptions about these factors.

225   All anchor points for the suspension of the chain hoist and the load should be of adequate strength and provided with effective high-security latching or locking systems.

226   All types of chain hoists should incorporate an automatic brake that permits smooth lowering of the load. It should be able to arrest and hold the load indefinitely without slip. The brake frictional materials should not be hazardous to health.

227   Pawls should be designed for effective engagement with the ratchet wheel, irrespective of any wear of frictional surfaces. Pawls should engage the ratchet using a spring (not a tension spring) or other positive means. Engagement should not depend solely on gravity. Twin pawls fitted with single heavy gauge springs are recommended for chain/lever hoists used offshore.

228   Power-driven chain hoists should incorporate suitable means of preventing overloads and be provided with an emergency stop located at the control station.

229   It should be impossible for the load chain to be run out beyond its working limit. A mechanical stop should be provided which prevents any overrun even when handling the test load (including the effects of shock and enhanced line pull).

230   Where the lifting range of the hook is extensive, a load chain bucket should be provided wherever possible.

231   Where chain hoists are suspended from trolleys, beams, padeyes etc, this suspension equipment should not be of lower rated capacity than the chain hoist. See *Lifting points and runway beams*, paragraphs 243-252.

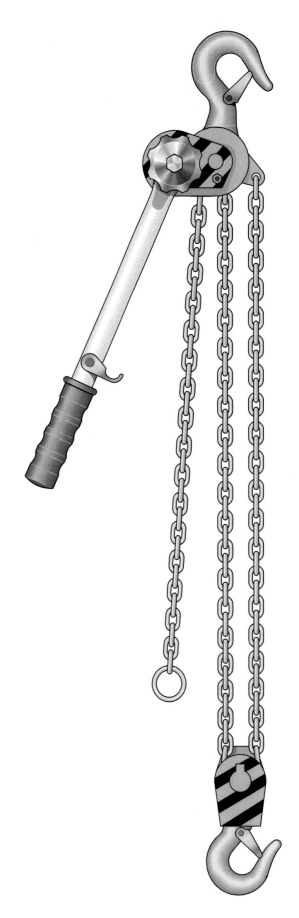

Figure 10 Lever hoist

Inspection

232   Chain hoists should be visually inspected before and after use. Any damage or faults should immediately be reported to the competent person and recorded.

Testing

233   When chain/lever hoists are subjected to an overload test, the test should ensure that each element in the drive system receives an overload by hoisting through the distance required to rotate every gear wheel at least once. Chain/lever hoists should also be subjected to a light load test to validate the effectiveness of the braking system under these conditions. The competent person should decide the magnitude of the light load. As a guide the British Standard (BS EN 13157: 2004[19]) recommends 2-5% of the SWL depending on the hoist capacity. Details of the overload and light load tests should be documented and validated by the competent person. The light load is meant for test purposes only and the chain hoist should not be used to lift loads of under 10% of the SWL for normal operations.

Operation

234   Manually-operated chain hoists should not be power driven under any circumstances or operated in any way other than that specified by the manufacturer or competent person.

235   Chain hoists should not be used for dragging or pulling equipment along the deck unless this is agreed by a competent person. Chain/lever hoists should not be used for lifting people.

236   People operating chain hoists should be experienced in their use/limitations and rigging practices. (See *Training,* paragraphs 83-91.)

237   Multiple chain hoists should not be used to perform a single lift unless assessed and supervised by a competent person (see paragraph 63.)

238   For powered chain hoists operated by pendant-type controllers, see paragraph 216.

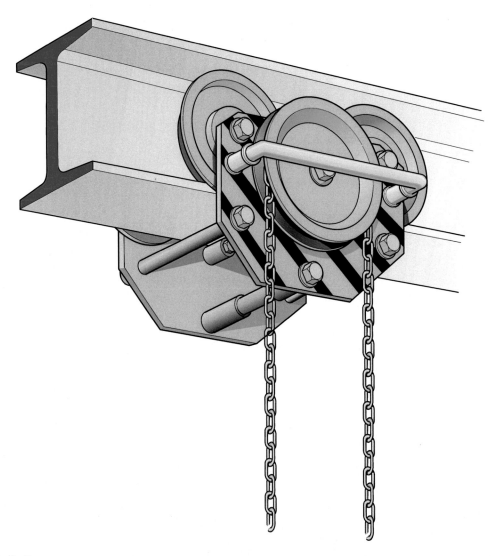

Figure 11 Trolley

Trolleys

Design and manufacture

239   Both powered and manually operated trolleys should be designed to remain captive with the runway beam under all circumstances, including the failure of one runner or wheel or its support.

240   The SWL should be clearly and legibly marked on the trolley. Any hoist unit having a greater rated load capacity than the trolley should not be used.

Selecting suitable equipment

241   On floating installations and vessels where motions could result in unsolicited movement of manually operated trolleys, all lifting operations using this type of equipment should be suspended. Powered trolleys should incorporate automatic braking and may be used during vessel motion up to the value of pitch/roll which the competent person has deemed is safe.

242   Trolleys which are used in potentially explosive atmospheres should incorporate non-sparking materials where appropriate. If electrical equipment is fitted, this should be suitably flame-proofed for use in these areas. See also paragraphs 74-77.

Lifting points and runway beams

Design and manufacture

243   Lifting points and runway beams should be designed to a recognised national, European or international standard.

244   The SWL of lifting points and runway beams should be clearly marked. The lifting equipment specified for use on the lifting point or runway beam should be identified.

245   The design of lifting points and runway beams should ensure that the lifting equipment and/or load is moved in a controlled manner as directed by the operator and that the lifting system remains stable at all times. Uncontrolled movement of the lifting point, runway beam, lifting equipment or load should be avoided.

Testing

246   Lifting points and runway beams should be inspected and tested to procedures agreed by a competent person. These procedures should be appropriate to the type of lifting equipment which will be suspended from these items.

247   You should ensure that details of materials, welding, examination and testing of lifting points and runway beams is documented, validated and approved by a competent person.

Selecting suitable equipment

248   The competent person should ensure the following are considered when assessing the design and suitability of lifting points and runway beams:

■   the magnitude and direction of operational, dynamic and overload forces (including overload testing);
■   the effects of non-equal load distribution;
■   the magnitude of all lateral forces;
■   forces induced by movements of the installation (floating installations);
■   forces induced during any transfer of the load to other lifting points or runway beam;
■   that the lifting point should be strong enough to resist tearing or shear out of any pierced part connecting the lifting appliance; and
■   that adequate contact area should be provided to prevent undue bearing pressures at connection points.

249   Lifting points and runway beams should be permanently installed and positively secured to the supporting structure. This should be designed to sustain the transmission of all loads generated. Portable lifting points such as beam clamps may be used where it is not possible to provide permanent lifting points. The competent person should ensure that all lifting points and runway beams are compatible with the lifting appliance to be used and that the connection of the appliance remains secure under all operating conditions.

250   Runway beams should be fitted with mechanical stops at each end of the beam. These should be of sufficient strength to prevent the trolley and its SWL from leaving the beam under all possible operational conditions.

251   Any lifting point, including tie-backs, pulling points and any ad-hoc lifting arrangement that has not been approved by a competent person should not be used.

Maintenance, repair and modification

252   Lifting points should be of smooth profile, free of defects, cuts etc (for example, which may have been caused by flame cutting equipment). Welding of lifting points should be carried out to recognised codes, standards and procedures. All welding should be undertaken only by coded welders. See also paragraphs 33-35.

Jacking systems

Design and manufacture

253   Jacking systems (other than self-elevating units) should be designed, constructed and maintained according to their intended use to the approval of a competent person.

Selecting suitable equipment

254   Jacks should have non-return check valves located immediately at their ports, to prevent any movement of the

piston if there is a hose/pipe burst, loss of hydraulic fluid or loss of supply power. The jacks should have an effective mechanical lock-out device which prevents any further load transmission to the hydraulic fluid once the jacked structure is in its final position.

255   The competent person should consider the following when assessing jacking systems:

■   a suitable allowance should be made for wind effects on the structure being jacked;
■   the maximum wind speed at which jacking operations should cease;
■   the jacks should be positively located at both the non-moving structure and at the structure being jacked, ensuring the jacks do not slide or tilt and that the jacked structure remains stable under all circumstances.

256   The jacking system should have a safe means of access during erection and operation. The system should not impede any evacuation or escape routes. Where jacking systems are deployed over the sea, you should consider the appropriate items of the section *Working harnesses/rope access systems,* paragraphs 295-307.

Operation

257   You should have procedures for safely abandoning the jacking operation and for effectively securing the jacked structure.

Maintenance, repair and modification

258   If attachment lugs or padeyes need to be welded or bolted onto existing structures, a competent person must approve this after fully assessing the implications to the original structural design.

Equipment for lifting people

Introduction

259   Before using cranes and other lifting equipment to transfer people, you should consider alternative methods of doing this.

Cranes

Design and manufacture

260   Cranes which are suitable for lifting people should be clearly marked at the crane operator's location 'SUITABLE FOR LIFTING PEOPLE' or 'SUITABLE FOR MAN-RIDING' and marked with the maximum number of people it can carry. Any crane that is not marked should not be used to lift people or for man-riding.

Selecting suitable equipment

261   Cranes used for lifting people should be equipped with hoist brakes that can be operated mechanically under all load conditions. The brakes should be able to support the specified test overload for the equipment.

262   The brakes should be automatically applied when the drive is in the 'OFF' or 'NEUTRAL' position, and on failure of the power supply to the motor or control device. The braking operation should be progressive, to avoid any shock loading of the hoisting system.

263   A second brake system should be provided for emergency use in case the normal braking system fails. For cranes this should be fitted to both load and boom hoist systems and be located as near to the hoist drums as possible. This brake should be strong enough to hold indefinitely the weight of the carrier/slings and the number of people carried. For hydraulic transmission system cranes (provided the system meets certain criteria), the braking effect of the hydraulic system itself would be considered as meeting the requirement for a secondary brake.

264   Clutches or other means of disengaging the drive train are prohibited for personnel-lifting operations. This is unless there is a fail-safe interface making it impossible to disengage the clutch when the drive train is in motion or when there is a load on the hook. Free-fall operation of load hoist or boom hoist systems is dangerous and should be avoided. See paragraph 192 for information on emergency load-release systems. Any speed-change gearbox should be of constant mesh type and designed so that it is not possible to change the gear ratio while the hoist system is carrying any load.

265   The crane should be fitted with an emergency stop located for the operator to use. It should be protected against accidental use. Operating the emergency stop should arrest all motions of the crane. In the event of failure to restart the prime mover, it should be possible to recover the carrier by manual methods.

Operation

266   Anyone being transported by crane needs to:

■   remain in full view of the crane operator; and
■   have all necessary personal safety equipment.

In addition, where people are transported over the sea, the requirements of the Offshore Installations (Prevention of Fire and Explosion, and Emergency Response) Regulations 1995 (PFEER)[20] should be complied with.

267   There are special recommendations for prime movers on cranes for man-riding purposes - see paragraphs 172-173.

Utility winches and winches used for lifting people

Design and manufacture

268   All winches used for lifting people should be clearly marked 'SUITABLE FOR LIFTING PEOPLE' or 'SUITABLE FOR MAN-RIDING'. Any winch that is not marked should not be used for lifting people.

Selecting suitable equipment

269   The following criteria should be considered for all winches:

■   The winch operating lever should automatically return to neutral when released.
■   Automatic brakes should be fitted so that they apply whenever the operating lever is returned to neutral or if there is loss of power to the drive or control system.

270   The following criteria should also apply when winches are used for lifting people:

■   A second independent brake should be provided for use if the automatic brake fails. This brake should be manually operated unless it is completely independent of the automatic braking system.
■   Devices should be incorporated in the winch system which prevent the personnel carrier from overriding, under-riding and overspeeding.
■   The winch should have adequate capacity to handle the line load itemised below with one wrap (number of complete turns along the drum width) of rope spooled on the drum:
    -   the nominal weight of passengers;
    -   the tare weight of the carrier; and
    -   the rope weight and friction effects.
    The sum of these weights should include an adequate safety factor together with a dynamic factor approved by a competent person.
■   The winch should be capable of lowering the carrier in a controlled manner in an emergency or if there is loss of power.

■ For winches that are sited on installations one or either of which could be moving relative to the other, such as motions between a semi-submersible and a fixed platform, then the brake holding capacity should be less than that generated by the minimum braking load of the rope and greater than that generated by the maximum line forces identified above.

■ The rope should be automatically spooled onto the winch drum to prevent bunching.

■ The design of the winch system should be confirmed by a hazard analysis and failure mode and effects analysis (FMEA) carried out by a competent person. The analysis should identify safety-critical elements which should undergo regular inspection, maintenance and function testing by the competent person(s).

Note: This requirement applies to transfer operations using personnel carriers and not to individual man-riding operations such as those carried out for drilling derrick inspections, maintenance etc where the individual is using a harness or Bosun's chair etc.

Operation

271 When winches are used for lifting people, the written operating procedure should include:

■ authority for use;
■ means of communication between the winch operator and passenger(s);
■ safety arrangements;
■ limiting conditions of use; and
■ training.

272 The operating procedures should include an assessment made by a competent person to ensure that any uncontrolled ascent of the carrier is prevented under all circumstances. This assessment should include calculations to ensure that the weight of the rope is never greater (including an adequate safety factor) on the winch side of the sheave system than the minimum weight on the carrying side of the sheave system.

273 The following criteria also apply:

■ Rope entanglement and undue wear should be prevented.

■ The rope should remain captive at all times around sheaves and at the winch drum.

■ The drum should be guarded to protect the operator if the rope should fail. The guard should not prevent the operator from viewing the spooling of the rope.

■ The line pull of the winch should be set so that if there is inadvertent snagging, any over-pull will not injure passengers. In certain types of operation, a higher line pull may be required for emergency man-riding recovery, for example from a moon pool. In this case, an override should be provided to increase the capacity of the winch to carry the extra weight of people and equipment needed to perform emergency operations. It is preferred however if the line pull for this type of winch is permanently set to allow a work basket with two persons to be carried.

274 Clutches or other methods of disengaging the drive system are dangerous and must be avoided. Where winches are to be used to lift people, a supervisor should be able to see them at all times. The supervisor should remain in direct communication with the winch operator throughout the operation.

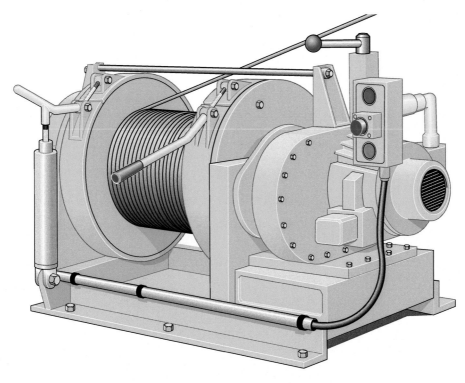

Figure 12 Man-riding winch

Note: Guard(s) removed for clarity

Personnel transportation equipment

Personnel carriers

275 Carriers used for personnel transfer operations should be designed so as to minimise the risk of persons being crushed, trapped, struck or falling from the carrier (LOLER regulation 5(1)(a)). For carriers that do not comply with LOLER, guidance is given in HSE Information Sheet reference 1/2007.[21]

Selecting suitable equipment

276 You or the competent person should ensure that carriers used for lifting people conform with the following:

■ The carrier is provided with slip-resistant floors and adequate drainage.
■ Items carried on the floor of the carrier are effectively secured.
■ The primary load line has the requisite safety factor. Where secondary or backup lines are used, a risk assessment should ensure that these do not increase risk. Load lines should be selected to ensure that the carrier does not spin or turn when lifted. All connections between the carrier and the lifting appliance should be unable to self-release under any circumstances.
■ In case the carrier should fall or be placed in the sea, it should be self-righting in all operational sea-states and with the most adverse passenger distribution on board. There should be procedures for the emergency recovery of people from the carrier or from the sea.
■ Carriers should be of a type which has been approved for use by a competent person and all necessary inspection, examination and test certificates should be current and be readily available for the regulatory authority (HSE) if so required.

Operation

277 You should ensure that all transfers of people by carrier are carried out to written procedures and that the operation is authorised by the OIM and supervised by a competent person. You should plan the use of personnel carriers to ensure that:

■ crane and winch operators have been specifically trained in transferring people by carrier and have experience of the type and use of the lifting equipment;
■ people who have not been involved in this kind of operation before are accompanied by someone who is familiar with the operation;
■ a risk assessment has been carried out. This should include consideration of environmental hazards;
■ during transfer over the sea, passengers are provided with survival suits and life jackets of an approved type. Additionally, effective emergency arrangements must be in place throughout the transfer as required by regulation 4 of PFEER;

■ The rescue and recovery arrangements must be capable of recovering people from the sea within specified performance standards. Where transfer operations over water are carried out in harbours, passengers should be provided with life jackets as a minimum requirement;
■ you avoid raising or lowering the personnel carrier near the propellers of a vessel. If this is not possible, the master of the vessel must terminate all propulsion if required;
■ where carriers are designed to lift a stretcher, the injured person must be accompanied by at least one other non-injured person during the transfer operation;
■ if seats are provided in the carrier, they are equipped with safety harnesses and instructions given for their use before commencing any transfer.

Personnel work baskets/platforms

Design and manufacture

278 The competent person should ensure that the design of the work basket/platform includes:

■ slip-resistant floors with adequate drainage to prevent any build-up of water;
■ effective means of securing all tools and loose gear safely within the basket and keeping them captive within the basket/platform if it is inadvertently spilled;
■ adequate anchor points or rails for the attachment of safety harnesses.

279 They should also ensure that:

■ the primary load line that connects the work basket/platform with the lifting appliance has the requisite safety factor. Where secondary or backup lines are used, a risk assessment should be made to ensure that these lines do not increase risk. All connections between the work basket and the lifting appliance should be unable to self-release under any circumstances.
■ the work basket/platform is clearly marked 'SUITABLE FOR THE TRANSFER OF PEOPLE'.
■ the work basket/platform has been approved for use by a competent person and all necessary inspection, examination and test certificates should be current and readily available for the Regulatory Authority (HSE) if required.

Selecting suitable equipment

280 You should only consider work baskets and platforms that are suspended from a crane or winch system when the assessed risk is the same or less than when using other reasonably practicable methods of transfer. You should consider using work staging instead of work baskets where reasonably practicable.

Operation

281 Any use of work baskets or platforms should be carried out to written procedures and supervised by a competent person. The competent person should not undertake these operations without your authorisation.

282 You should plan the use of work baskets to ensure that:

- crane or winch operators have been specifically trained in the use of work baskets and are experienced with the type and use of the lifting equipment;
- at least one person in the work basket is familiar with these operations and remains in radio contact with the crane or winch operator, banksman and supervisor at all times;
- a risk assessment has been carried out. This should include consideration of environmental hazards;

- work baskets, platforms and associated equipment are checked before use by a competent person;
- people working from the basket or platform wear a safety harness throughout the operation;
- during transfer over the sea, passengers are provided with survival suits and life jackets of an approved type. Additionally, effective emergency arrangements must be in place throughout the transfer as required by regulation 4 of PFEER. The rescue and recovery arrangements must be capable of recovering people from the sea within specified performance standards. Where transfer operations over water are carried out in harbours, passengers should be provided with life jackets as a minimum requirement;
- all key people, including the crane operator and banksman, remain on station throughout the operation; and
- all instructions about locating, movement and station keeping of the work basket are clearly conveyed by a competent person.

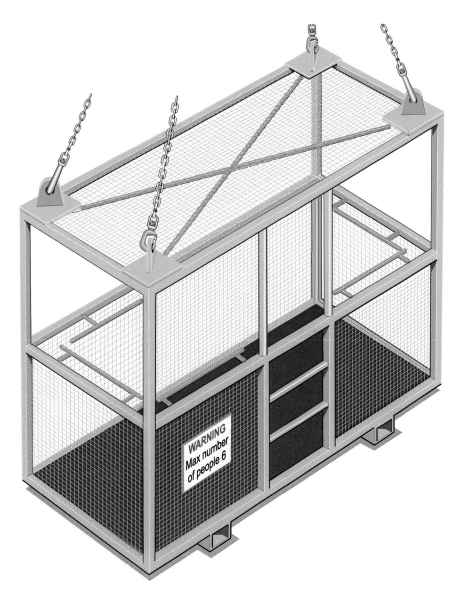

Figure 13 Personnel carrier

Passenger lifts

283   Where lifts are used for carrying passengers, you should also consider providing:

- an overload alarm and overload protection system;
- space for a stretcher and medical staff;
- adequate lighting with emergency backup inside the lift and lift well;
- suitable communication systems;
- adequate safety equipment including:
- smoke detection systems and smoke hoods;
- fire extinguisher(s);
- gas detection systems;
- personal safety equipment for the full complement of passengers; and
- effective emergency escape routes/escape systems which can also be used during a power failure.

Equipment used in drilling and associated operations for carrying people

Casing stabbing boards

Design and manufacture

284   The hoisting system should be designed and constructed to codes and standards agreed with the competent person. Any rack and pinion system should be designed so that the working platform will not fall if the rack or pinion should fail. Where winch systems are used, the rope should spool evenly on the drum and there should be at least three full turns of rope remaining on the drum at all times. The rope should remain captive with the drum and sheave systems under all service conditions, including slack rope conditions. Upper and lower-level limit switches should ensure that the hoist system does not operate beyond its specified range.

285   Casing stabbing boards should be clearly marked 'SUITABLE FOR CARRYING PEOPLE' and with the number of people they can carry.

Selecting suitable equipment

286   Casing stabbing boards and other working platforms that are raised and lowered by a powered or manually operated system should provide users with a secure and safe means of travel and support at the point of work.

287   The working platform should be positively guided by rails or runners. The guidance system should ensure that the platform remains captive to its rails or runners under all circumstances, including any wheel or roller failure or failure of the primary hoisting system.

288   Rails/runners should be securely attached to their supports and should not open up under:

- static operations;
- travelling or other dynamic operations;

- overload testing; or
- operation of the secondary control/braking system.

289   The working platform should have non-slip standing surfaces, handrails, midrails and edge protection. The platform should also have anchorage points for inertia-type safety harnesses.

290   Control of the primary lifting system should provide smooth movement of the working platform. The control lever should spring to neutral on release, effectively braking the primary hoisting system. Where a manual system of raising or lowering the platform is used, a positive locking system such as a ratchet-and-pawl mechanism should be provided in addition to the service brake. A secondary, inertia-type brake, acting at the rails, should be provided in case there is any failure in the primary hoisting system. The secondary brake should act independently of the primary brake and not require any power source (hydraulic, electrical or pneumatic) for its operation.

291   Each braking system should be capable of holding the full rated capacity of the loaded stabbing board plus allowances for dynamic effects. It should not be possible to lower the working platform by brake operation only.

292   A speed-controlling device should be provided to prevent the raising and lowering of the working platform from exceeding its prescribed tripping speed.

293   Casing stabbing boards and all other working platforms which are positioned by a hydraulically powered arm-type system should have high-integrity seals in the hydraulic rams which actuate the arm. Built-in check valves should be fitted at the ram ports to prevent any movement of the ram if there is a hose or pipe burst.

Testing

294   Casing stabbing boards should be regularly tested with the maximum rated load. Inspection should include the functioning of control and braking systems, condition of ropes, structural fixings, padeyes and safety systems.

Working harnesses and rope access systems

Selecting suitable equipment

295   Working harnesses and rope access systems may be used where it is not otherwise practical to provide safer methods of access such as scaffolding or mobile working platforms. A risk assessment should be made by a competent person before these systems are used.

296   Working harnesses and associated equipment should be to recognised standards.

297   Rope access systems should incorporate an overspeed descent device.

298   The competent person should provide written operating procedures and should also ensure that:

- all components have adequate duty and safety factors appropriate to intended service;
- anchorage points are dedicated for use and specific to the type of equipment used. They should provide high-security fixing and be at least as strong as that of the rope;
- in addition to the primary working rope, a secondary safety rope is provided which must be available on demand to automatically arrest any uncontrolled descent of the user;
- all connectors are designed to prevent inadvertent disconnection;
- emergency procedures are in place;
- environmental and other influencing factors have been identified to define limits of use and that permits to work are provided as appropriate;
- a certificate of proof load test or certificate of conformity appropriate to the type of equipment or materials used has been provided by a verification body; and
- components used in the rope access system have been permanently and clearly marked.

Inspection

299   Rope access equipment, including anchorages and harness, should be inspected by the user before and after use and at intervals agreed with the manufacturer and the competent person. Users should be trained to inspect equipment. Any damage or defects should be recorded and reported to a competent person.

Operation

300   All staff involved with rope deployment or access systems should be supervised by a qualified competent person. Under no circumstances should users assume this responsibility or operate this equipment unsupervised.

301   All staff involved with rope access operations should be able to communicate at all times via two-way radios.

302   Hand tools and materials carried to the work point should be firmly secured to the harness. When in use they should be prevented from falling free. Heavy components should be lifted independently by a lifting appliance or system which is approved by a competent person.

303   Users should have suitable protective clothing appropriate to the work task. When working over the sea or a moon pool, they should wear life jackets.

Maintenance, repair and modification

304   Additional or replacement components, agreed by the competent person, should be compatible with others used in the system and should comply with the manufacturer's original specifications. Details of replacement components, repairs, modifications etc should be documented by a competent person.

305   Rope access equipment should be maintained and stored in accordance with the manufacturer's instructions.

Where equipment has been subjected to a saline environment, it should be hosed down with fresh water and thoroughly dried before storage.

306   For powered winches used as part of a rope access system, see paragraphs 268-274.

Training

307   Everyone involved with the use of rope access equipment should be trained and competent to carry out their tasks on the type of equipment in use. Training should preferably be undertaken through a training body approved by OPITO (the Offshore Petroleum Industry Training Organisation) or similar body. Records of the level of training, experience and competency of each user should be validated by a competent person.

Drilling equipment

Introduction

308   Drilling equipment covered in this section includes:

- drilling hoisting systems;
- compensators and tensioners;
- blow-out preventer (BOP) handling equipment; and
- drill pipe and casing handling equipment.

Design and manufacture

309   This equipment, with its foundations, fixings and attachments, should be designed, constructed, maintained and operated according to national, European or international standards or to standards and controls agreed between the equipment supplier and the competent person. All primary structural, mechanical components and all pressure containment vessels or systems should be traceable according to a recognised quality standard. For details of personnel-carrying equipment used in drilling operations, see paragraphs 284-307.

Testing

310   Details of load testing and pressure testing at the supplier's works and at the installation should be documented and have signed approval by a competent person. The competent person should ensure that the design of the equipment includes adequate safety factors appropriate to the intended service loads, frequency of use and environmental and other operational limitations.

311   For equipment used in potentially explosive atmospheres, see paragraphs 74-77.

Training

312   You should ensure that staff working with drilling equipment have received adequate training specific to the type of equipment used.

Drilling hoisting systems

Selecting suitable equipment

313   There have been rapid developments in the design and operation of drilling hoisting systems. These developments have been advanced by the drilling industry in keeping with new technologies and have improved operational safety at and in the vicinity of the workplace.

314   There are now several types and configurations of drilling hoisting systems in use offshore. The competent person should consider those which may be appropriate.

315   Where a mechanical coupling or clutch is fitted between the 'auxiliary' brake and the drilling hoisting system drum, a system should be provided which prevents any inadvertent disengagement of the 'auxiliary' brake. It should not be possible to disengage the friction brake until the clutch for the 'auxiliary' brake has been engaged.

316   Hoisting systems which use hydrodynamic auxiliary brakes or retarders should have equipment that effectively monitors the temperature, flow and level of the working fluid.

317   For AC and hydraulically powered drilling hoisting systems, the friction brakes should be applied automatically when:

- the emergency stop is activated; or
- the electrical or hydraulic power has failed.

The brakes should be dynamically rated for emergency use, taking account of the speed and the combined weight of the travelling block and string load.

318   Hydraulically powered brakes should have an emergency backup system. The pressure of both primary and emergency hydraulic systems should be monitored. For disc brake systems, the discs should be water-cooled.

319   Under emergency conditions it should be possible to lower the load in a controlled manner within the rig structure to a safe and secure position. This applies to all types of drilling hoisting systems.

320   The emergency stop should automatically activate if:

- potentially dangerous faults occur within the electromagnetic braking system; or
- the kinetic energy of the travelling block and load exceeds the limiting threshold.

321   The braking system may be a combination of electromagnetic and friction braking. It should be of adequate capacity to retard and hold the travelling block and the maximum string load when the emergency stop is activated.

322   Programmable logic control systems should be of high integrity and incorporate self-diagnostic healthy status systems. They may be used for managing:

- the kinetic energy of the travelling block and string load;
- impending overloads;
- overspeeding;
- the prevention of overhoisting or overlowering; and
- work done by the hoist rope.

Testing

323   For hoisting systems which use electromagnetic brakes or retarders, you should consider monitoring:

- the temperature and flow rate of the cooling water supply for the brake coils;
- the status and condition of the electromagnetic braking system; and
- the kinetic energy of the travelling block and the load.

324   For ac-powered drilling hoisting systems, the temperature of the motor rotor should be monitored.

Operation

325   Where the effectiveness of the braking system depends on the electromagnetic brake, the brake coils should be connected to an uninterrupted power supply (UPS) for use on demand if there is loss of the primary power source. An ac drilling hoisting system should be provided with UPS for control and monitoring systems. If the UPS is provided by batteries, they should be kept fully charged. The charge and condition of the batteries should be monitored. If the emergency UPS is not available, an alarm at the control point should activate.

326   Provision should be made to:

- warn the control station of impending overloads;
- prevent overspeeding; and
- prevent overhoisting or overlowering.

327   You should consider a method to prevent collisions between the travelling block system and other equipment operating at the drill floor and within the derrick.

328   Control cabins and control systems should be protected against the weather, and ergonomically designed. Seating should be provided for the driller and driller's assistant. The control cabin should be located to allow a clear view of activities at the drill floor and within the derrick. It should be protected against falling or swinging objects. Where the driller cannot directly view the spooling of the rope at the drilling hoisting system drum, the drum should be monitored at the console via a CCTV system.

329   Wire ropes should conform to and be used in accordance with a recognised standard, eg API RP 9B.[22] A competent person should consider the following recommendations:

- The groove profile dimensions and hardness levels for drums and sheaves should be compatible with the rope diameter, its construction and grade of wire. Any changes to the rope specification should not be made without the approval of a competent person.
- The ratio of the diameter of the drum/sheave to the diameter of the wire rope (D/d) should be as large as practicable to maximise the fatigue life of the rope.
- The number of layers of rope spooled onto the drawworks drum should be kept to a minimum: no more than three layers are recommended. The rope should be spooled under as much tension as possible to maintain an even spooling pattern and prevent the underlying rope coils being crushed, abraded or distorted by the oncoming rope. Slack rope should be avoided. Fleet angles should be maintained as specified by the equipment supplier.
- Ropes should remain captive to the drum and sheaves under all operating conditions.
- Ropes should have adequate safety factors appropriate to their service duties, the effect of friction at sheaves and any reverse bends in the rope system. Reverse bends in rope systems should be avoided wherever possible.

- The work done by the rope, ie the sum of all round-trip drilling operations, should be monitored and recorded at the driller's control console (this work is defined as all operational loads on the rope multiplied by the distance travelled by the rope, expressed in tonne mile units). This data should be used to assess when to slip and cut the rope to obtain even wear in the rope system and to ensure that further drilling operations can be continued safely. Rope which has been slipped and cut should be inspected before discard to check whether any adjustment to the tonne mile assessment procedure may be required.
- Rope terminations and anchor points, for example at the dead line anchor and at the drilling hoisting system winch drum, should be of adequate strength and should not cause damage to the rope. These terminations should be located to permit easy in-situ inspection. Rope terminations using wire rope grips are not recommended for primary load path anchorages.

Heave compensated drilling hoisting systems

330   On floating installations, when compensation for the motions of the installation/vessel is provided directly by the drilling hoisting system winch drum, the following should be considered:

- The control system should be self-diagnostic. Unhealthy status of the system should be signalled at the driller's control console. The system should give prior warning of any impending automatic shutdown.
- The assessment and monitoring of the work done by the rope (see paragraph 329) should take account of the additional 'trips' made by the rope when compensators are used.
- Consideration should be given to particular safety features for heave compensators such as speed control valves, automatic air shut-off valves and lockbar check valves.

These recommendations are additional to those listed in paragraphs 313-329.

Crown-mounted heave compensators

331   For crown-mounted compensating systems where the wire rope of the drawworks is passed over the sheaves of the compensator, the appropriate factors listed in paragraph 308 should be considered. Additional recommendations are:

- The compensating cylinders should be cushioned at each end of the stroke to prevent undue shock loads arising in the system.
- If the drill string should break, excessive speed extension of the cylinders should be automatically controlled within predetermined limits.

■ Air, hydraulic pressure, hydraulic oil levels and stroke position should be monitored at the driller's control console.

Drill string heave compensators

332 Drill string heave compensators may be fitted at the travelling block to provide motion compensation via a system of chains in lieu of wire ropes. A competent person should consider, as appropriate, the recommendations on wire ropes in paragraphs 114-117.

Guideline and riser tensioners

333 For systems used to maintain tension in guidelines and risers on floating installations and vessels, a competent person should consider, as appropriate, the recommendations in paragraphs 114-117. In addition, primarily for deep water operations, there should be a way of effectively controlling:

■ cylinder extension velocity, as may occur when a guideline breaks; and
■ the kinetic energy of the system which may arise during emergency disconnection of the riser.

The control should prevent any upward motion of the riser that may otherwise cause the riser to impact with the installation or vessel.

Blow-out preventers

334 Where blow-out preventers (BOPs) are deployed sub-sea using a wire rope guideline system, the forces on the guideline system should be considered under limits of operation and should include, for example, the effects of wave slam and sea current forces. For BOPs handled by a gantry/beam crane mounted within the substructure of the derrick, see paragraphs 203-210.

335 Equipment for handling BOPs should have a control system that facilitates inching of the hoist, lower and travel systems.

Pipe handling equipment

336 The suitability of equipment for lifting and handling drill pipe, drill collars, casing jars, tools etc should be assessed to ensure that:

■ wheeled or travelling equipment remains captive with its rail or guidance system;
■ drilling tubulars, tools etc, which are conveyed via chute or trough skid systems are prevented from spilling from the handling appliance;
■ handling systems which use powered grips or clamps for carrying drilling tubulars will maintain their full retention capability if there is any power loss or system failure;

■ there is effective means of preventing the lifting equipment or load from colliding with other equipment; and
■ all equipment incorporates an emergency stop system and ready means for isolating power supplies.

Appendix 1:
Guidance referring to LOLER and PUWER

Guidance section	Paragraph number	Applicable LOLER Regulation No.	Applicable PUWER Regulation No.
Introduction and regulations	1-15	2,3	3, and ACOP pages 11, 13
Regulations LOLER/PUWER	9-15	3	3
Selecting suitable equipment	16-29	4, 9	4, 5
Operating the equipment	68-77	8, 9	8
Planning the use of lifting equipment	59-67	6, 8	4, 8, 12
Training	83-91		7, 9
Marking	78-82	7, Item 3 Schedule	23
Inspection	47-51	9	6
Documentation, reports and test details	52-55	9, 10, 11	8
Material selection	30-32	ACOP page 13	
Welding	33-35	ACOP page 13	
Corrosion protection	36-39	ACOP page 13	
Access and escape	40-46	ACOP page 14	
Slewing cranes	92-202	4	4, 14, 15, 16, 17, 18, 19
Overhead/gantry cranes and hoists	203-218	4	4
Chain hoists	219-238	4	4
Trolleys	239-242	4	4
Lifting points and runway beams	243-252	4	4
Jacking systems	253-258	4	4
Lifting personnel	259-307	5	7
Drilling equipment	308-336	4	4

Appendix 2:
Glossary

Glossary terms

ac	alternating current
ACOP	Approved Code of Practice
AOGBO	Health and Safety at Work etc Act 1974 (Application Outside Great Britain) Order 2001
BOP	blow-out preventer
CCTV	closed-circuit television
FMEA	failure mode and effects analysis
GOP	gross overload protection
HSE	Health and Safety Executive
HSW Act	Health and Safety at Work etc Act 1974
LEEA	Lifting Equipment Engineers Association
LOLER	Lifting Operations and Lifting Equipment Regulations 1998
MHSWR	Management of Health and Safety at Work Regulations 1999
MAR	Offshore Installations and Pipeline Works (Management and Administration) Regulations 1995
NDT	non-destructive testing
OIM	offshore installation manager
PA	public address
PFEER	Offshore Installations (Prevention of Fire and Explosion, and Emergency Response) Regulations 1995
PUWER	Provision and Use of Work Equipment Regulations 1998
RCI	Rated Capacity Indicator
SLI	safe load indicator (also known as Rated Capacity Indicator)
SSW	safe system of work
SWL	safe working load
UPS	uninterrupted power supply

References

1   *Lifting Operations and Lifting Equipment Regulations 1998* SI 1998/2307 The Stationery Office 1998 ISBN 978 0 11 079598 0

2   *Provision and Use of Work Equipment Regulations 1998* SI 1998/2306 The Stationery Office 1998 ISBN 978 0 11 079599 7

3   *Health and Safety at Work etc Act 1974 (Application Outside Great Britain) Order 2001* SI 2001/2127 The Stationery Office 2001 ISBN 978 0 11 029567 1

4   Maritime and Coastguard Agency, MCA Infoline: Tuthead, Mumbles, Swansea SA3 4HW Tel: 0870 600 6505

5   *Manual Handling Operations Regulations 1992* SI 1992/2793 The Stationery Office 1992 ISBN 978 0 11 025920 8

6   *Manual handling. Manual Handling Operations Regulations 1992 (as amended). Guidance on Regulations* L23 (Third edition) HSE Books 2004 ISBN 978 0 7176 2823 0

7   *Safe use of lifting equipment. Lifting Operations and Lifting Equipment Regulations 1998. Approved Code of Practice and guidance* L113 HSE Books 1998 ISBN 978 0 7176 1628 2

8   *Safe use of work equipment. Provision and Use of Work Equipment Regulations 1998. Approved Code of Practice and guidance* L22 (Second edition) HSE Books 1998 ISBN 978 0 7176 1626 8

9   *Offshore Installations and Pipeline Works (Management and Administration) Regulations 1995* The Stationery Office 1995 SI 1995/738 ISBN 978 0 11 052735 2

10   *Management of Health and Safety at Work Regulations 1999* SI 1999/3242 The Stationery Office 1999 ISBN 978 0 11 085625 4

11   BS 7121-11: 1998 *Code of practice for safe use of cranes. Offshore cranes* British Standards Institution ISBN 978 0 580 29503 4

12   BS EN 12385: 2000 *Steel wire ropes. Safety. Parts 1, 2, 3 and 4* British Standards Institution

13   BS EN 13411-3: 2004 *Terminations for steel wire ropes. Safety. Metal and resin socketing* British Standards Institution

14   BS 3692: 2001 *ISO metric precision hexagon bolts, screws and nuts. Specification* British Standards Institution ISBN 978 0 580 33262 3

15   BS ISO 4406: 1999 *Hydraulic fluid power. Fluids. Method for coding the level of contamination by solid particles* British Standards Institution ISBN 978 0 580 34182 3

16   BS 7262: 1990 *Specification for automatic safe load indicators* British Standards Institution ISBN 978 0 580 18145 0

17   BS EN 12077-2: 1999 *Cranes safety. Requirements for health and safety. Limiting and indicating devices* British Standards Institution ISBN 978 0 580 30990 8

18   *Code of practice for the selection, management, use, maintenance and examination of hand chain blocks and lever hoists in the offshore environment (including sub-sea)* LEEA033 Lifting Equipment Engineers Association

19   BS EN 13157: 2004 *Cranes. Safety. Hand powered lifting equipment* British Standards Institution ISBN 978 0 580 45420 2

20   *Offshore Installations (Prevention of Fire and Explosion, and Emergency Response) Regulations 1995* SI 1995/743 The Stationery Office ISBN 978 0 11 052751 2

21   *Guidance on the transfer of personnel by carriers* Information Sheet 1/2007 HSE 2007 www.hse.uk/offshore/infosheets/is1-2007.pdf

22   *Recommended Practice on Application, Care, and Use of Wire Rope for Oilfield Service* API Recommended Practice 9B (Eleventh Edition) American Petroleum Institute 2002

23   BS EN 13414: 2003 *Steel wire rope slings Parts 1-3* British Standards Institution

For information about health and safety, or to report inconsistencies or inaccuracies in this guidance, visit www.hse.gov.uk/. You can view HSE guidance online and order priced publications from the website. HSE priced publications are also available from bookshops.

British Standards can be obtained in PDF or hard copy formats from BSI: http://shop.bsigroup.com or by contacting BSI Customer Services for hard copies only Tel: 020 8996 9001 email: cservices@bsigroup.com.

The Stationery Office publications are available from The Stationery Office, PO Box 29, Norwich NR3 1GN Tel: 0870 600 5522 Fax: 0870 600 5533 email: customer.services@tso.co.uk Website: www.tsoshop.co.uk/ (They are also available from bookshops.) Statutory Instruments can be viewed free of charge at www.legislation.gov.uk/.